A History of Mathematics

FOR SECONDARY SCHOOLS

A History of Mathematics

FOR SECONDARY SCHOOLS

by H. A. Freebury

CASSELL · LONDON

CASSELL & COMPANY LTD
35 Red Lion Square · London WC1
and at
MELBOURNE·SYDNEY·TORONTO
JOHANNESBURG·CAPE TOWN·AUCKLAND

© Cassell & Co. Ltd 1958
First edition March 1958
Second edition September 1960
Third edition August 1964

Printed in Great Britain by
The Camelot Press Ltd., London and Southampton
564

PREFACE

THOUGH the mature reader may find this book useful as a brief and elementary introduction to a more intensive study, he is asked to bear in mind that it has been written mostly for the younger student. Consequently the style and explanation may seem rather tedious, for every effort has been made to keep the subject matter and vocabulary such that it can be understood by the average pupil working at G.C.E. Ordinary Level.

To the latter it is recommended that he should first read the work in the order in which it is written. Book IV deals with individual topics, and as it sometimes enlarges on those dealt with in previous Books, explanations are less numerous.

It is hoped that this volume will stimulate the reader's interest in mathematics as a whole, emphasising its unique importance and presenting it as the expanding achievement of many great minds throughout the ages. If these aims are really accomplished a valuable method of approach will be open to both the teaching and learning of mathematics in general in secondary education.

My acknowledgments are due to the Senate of the University of London for permission to use the numerous examination questions from previous G.C.E. papers which appear after most chapters.

Finally, I wish to record my deep gratitude for the interest shown from the beginning by my colleague Mr. E. L. Hayward, B.Sc. His wide experience has been placed freely at my disposal, and his criticisms and valuable suggestions have made a substantial contribution to this volume.

H. A. FREEBURY

CONTENTS

Book One

EARLY TIMES

Book Two

THE FOURTH TO THE SIXTEENTH CENTURIES

CONTENTS   ix

Book Three
THE SEVENTEENTH CENTURY AND AFTER

Book Four

TOPICS OF PARTICULAR INTEREST

Book One

EARLY TIMES

INTRODUCTORY

THE BEGINNING OF NUMBERS

CIVILIZATION really began when our ancestors gave up their wanderings and learned to settle peaceably into groups, or what we call communities. Probably attracted to the river valleys in the first place by the animals he was hunting, early man saw all the advantages of living near a constant water supply, especially when, as happens in some parts of the world, the river banks are left covered with a new rich layer of soil following the seasonal flooding of the river.

As you might guess, large settlements grew up alongside the river Nile in Egypt, the Tigris and the Euphrates in Mesopotamia (which really means 'the land between the rivers'), alongside the Indus—and later the Ganges—in India, and the Hwang-ho—and later the Yangtse—in China. Other settlements were taking place, of course, but the ones just mentioned are the most important as regards the subsequent development of mankind.

In the first part of this book we shall deal chiefly with Egypt and Mesopotamia; that is, with the valleys of the Nile, the Tigris and the Euphrates. Yet we must constantly bear in mind that a somewhat similar development was taking place in these other parts of the world.

No one knows when the idea of numbers first arose, but it was many thousands of years ago. Probably, large numbers were of little use to our ancestors until they had learned to tame animals, when they found that they needed to count their sheep and cows to make sure that none had been lost or stolen. They soon realized that it was best to count them in groups, and the most obvious number grouping was that of 5 or 10, as the fingers on the hands. So, you see, our early ancestors counted on their

3

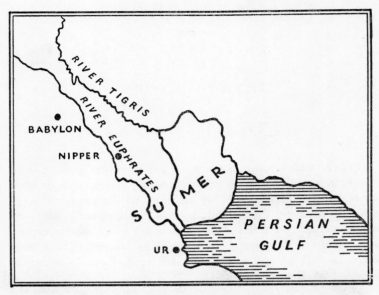

Sketch Map of Sumer and the Two Rivers

fingers just as young children do today, and we find that in most number systems throughout history, 5 or some multiple of 5 (that is, 10, 20 or 60), is used as the base; though there is one number system called Syriac arranged in 2's and 4's (two hands and two feet).

In South America some tribes, even today, give special names to a group of 5 (one hand), 10 (two hands), 15 (two hands and one foot), and 20 (two hands and two feet). Indeed, our score, referred to frequently in the Bible, probably began in this way.

However, as man's possessions increased, an improvement was needed in counting and with it some means of setting down, that is, of recording, numbers. This was sometimes done by cutting notches on a stick, tying knots in a sinew or a vine, or by means of pebbles arranged in groups of 5's or 10's. Soon the need was felt to indicate 10 by some other means, by some special sign, more correctly called a symbol.

Once this symbol was accepted, numbers could be set down with reference to it, so that larger numbers could be recorded. 10, we say today, was used as a base. In our own system, for instance, 15 means not $1+5$, but $10+5$.

Meanwhile man had become more and more civilized. He felt the need for trade with neighbouring communities, and this led, in turn, to further developments in counting and recording numbers. Much larger numbers were found to be necessary. They were placed into a larger group and given a different symbol, so that they could be written down more quickly.

All this took thousands of years. Our present number system, called the decimal position system, is an improvement on earlier methods and has allowed the science of mathematics to grow to what it is today.

As you will see, the development of our number system, and of mathematics in general, is really an interesting story.

1: MESOPOTAMIA

PART ONE—THE DAWN OF TRADE

H E R E are some names and dates that will help you as you read
this chapter. The dates are only approximate, for there was
considerable overlapping.

Sumerians	4000–2000 B.C.
Babylonians	2000–1700 B.C.
Various	
Kingdoms	1700–800 B.C.
Assyrians	800–600 B.C.
Chaldeans	600–500 B.C.

As we have already seen, the rich valleys of the Tigris and
Euphrates attracted settlers. If you look on the map you will
see a land called Sumer lying between the two rivers at the
entrance to the Persian Gulf, and the people who settled in this
region around 4000 B.C. were called Sumerians.

Their harvests here were plentiful, often eighty times the
sowing, and because of this abundance of crops it was seen that
it was unnecessary for everyone to grow his own food. Man
could now specialize.

For instance, one man could do building all the time, another
could do weaving of cloth, a third might make implements or
weapons. Also, as these people had a crude religion, temples were
built and priests supported by the workers lived in these and
controlled much of the life of the people.

Just as thousands of years before in the Stone Age, man had
bartered his possessions using such things as amber or flint as
a means of exchange, so the Sumerian could now barter his
goods with food as a means of exchange. In other words, barley

B   7

or wheat would serve a similar purpose to him then as money does to us today. If you had a bow and some arrows worth 4 measures of barley and wished to exchange these for a goat considered worth 8 measures of barley, you could carry out the deal providing you handed over the 4 measures of barley required to make up the difference in values.

Later, as precious metals such as gold and silver were discovered and became more plentiful, it was seen that they were a much more convenient means of exchange. Pieces of silver weighing $\frac{1}{60}$ of a lb. and called a shekel were introduced, so that values could now be estimated in weights of silver. When gold appeared it was considered worth 4 times that of silver until the latter was more plentiful; then its value dropped until it was worth only $\frac{1}{15}$ that of gold.

This trading grew to such an extent that it was necessary to keep records of most transactions. As clay was abundant in these parts the recording was done in clay. The clay was flattened out into tablets and a reed or bone called a stylus, resembling a pencil but circular at one end and shaped to a triangle at the other, was used for marking the tablet. When this was done, the tablet was allowed to dry in the sun. Thousands of these tablets have been discovered and deciphered during the past 100 years, and they tell us countless things about the ways and lives of the people of those days.

In particular, these tablets show us that many of the business methods we use today, such as rates of interest and credit, were used in principle some 4,000 years ago, and had a great influence upon the lives of the people.

When later we come to the Babylonians, we hear of a great king called Hammurabi, who reigned between 1948 and 1905 B.C. Among other things Hammurabi set down a code of laws which strictly regulated the lives of his subjects, and under such control life in these parts prospered as never before.

We have already mentioned the temples, and as well as carrying out religious activities, these were also the centres of business. All government taxes were paid into the temple, and as these were paid mostly in grain, large storehouses were necessary.

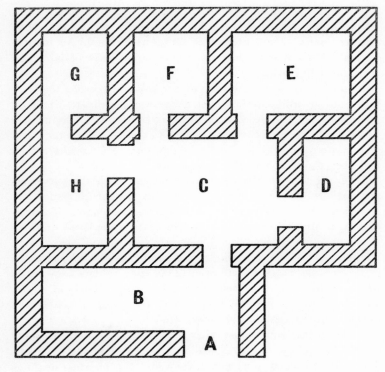

A BABYLONIAN SCHOOLHOUSE

Diagram of the ground plan of the oldest known schoolhouse in the
world, in use about 1900 B.C. in Babylonia. Its remains are still
standing after being uncovered, and on the floor were found the clay
tablets on which the boys and girls had worked their exercises.

A Entrance
B Entrance Hall. The doorkeeper sat at the end of this room near
the door.
C An open courtyard, corresponding to a small playground.
D, E, F, G, H Classrooms.

(Diagram reproduced from *Ancient Times* by J. H. Breasted, by
kind permission of the publishers, Messrs. Ginn & Co.)

The temples acted also as banks, though the only coinage was silver lumps valued by weight, as already mentioned; they granted loans, at an interest of 20%, which could be paid in monthly instalments; they controlled large areas of land and often dealt in goods.

Another activity of the temple was to train persons for business and government. A school house was usually to be found in or near the temple. One of these at the time of Hammurabi has actually been discovered, with the exercises of the boys and girls written on clay tablets and lying on the floor where they had been placed some 4,000 years ago.

Later still, under the Assyrians, dealings with the surrounding nations brought an even greater expansion of trade, and Assyrian merchants were to be found in most parts of southeast Asia Minor. By now, silver had entirely replaced grain as a means of exchange. Small bars, rods or round pieces were stamped with their value in weight, and also carried the name of the temple which had minted them. Clay tablets were made which stated that they represented so many shekels of silver, and were sent in advance as payment for goods, probably the first cheques or postal orders ever sent!

From all this you will see that we should be grateful to these people for many of our so-called modern methods. For undoubtedly the idea of coined money and the business dealings mentioned above came in the first place from this part of the world.

PART TWO—GENERAL MATHEMATICS. THE RECORDING OF NUMBERS, THE SEXAGESIMAL SYSTEM, UNIT FRACTIONS, METHODS OF CALCULATION

A. The Recording of Numbers

We have seen that the keeping of records and the recording of numbers became necessary with the growth of trade. We will now see how the Sumerians and Babylonians recorded and dealt with numbers.

You have already heard of the stylus and clay tablet. To show numbers from 1 to 9 the Sumerian used either end of the stylus and pushed it obliquely into the clay tablet to make an impression like this 〉 or this ٢. Usually the symbols were arranged in rows of three, so that 6 might be written as:

$$\begin{matrix} 〉 & 〉 & 〉 \\ 〉 & 〉 & 〉 \end{matrix} \quad \text{or as} \quad \begin{matrix} ٢ & ٢ & ٢ \\ ٢ & ٢ & ٢ \end{matrix}$$

For 10 and its multiples either a circle was made, by holding the stylus upright when pushing it into the clay, or a triangle, by holding the triangular end from left to right.

Thus: ◉ or ◄ stood for 10

Unfortunately, for it makes it more difficult to understand, the symbol for 1 served also for 60, 60^2 (3,600), 60^3 and so on; while the symbol for 10 served also for 10×60, 10×60^2 and so on. Only by reading through the accounts, or the passage concerned (what we call the context), could you decide which number was intended.

Here are some numbers as set down by the Sumerians with their meanings alongside them:

◄ ◄ ٢ = 10 + 10 + 1 = 21. ◉ ◉ 〉 〉 〉 = 10 + 10 + 3 = 23.

٢ ٢ ◄ ◄ ◄ ٢ ⋇ = 60 + 60 + 10 + 10 + 10 + 10 + 10 + 1 + $\frac{1}{2}$ = $171\frac{1}{2}$
(note the sign for $\frac{1}{2}$.)

By studying the last number you can see for yourself how the same sign was used for 60 and 1 according to its position. At the same time you may wonder why the two 60's are used. We will now discuss this.

B. The Sexagesimal System

To show a 60 when indicating a quantity of beer, a semi-circle was made with a larger stylus, and in earlier times the same symbol stood for 100 when grain was being measured. So for a time two systems were in use, a decimal one such as our own, based on 10's, and another, as you see from the number $171\frac{1}{2}$ above, based on 60's. Gradually the decimal system fell into disuse, so that by 2,500 B.C. only the system based on 60's was used. Such a system is called a Sexagesimal System, and was the basis of reckoning throughout Mesopotamia.

Why the Sumerians chose 60 as a base is not really known. They knew that the side of a regular hexagon inscribed in a circle is equal to the radius of the circumscribing circle; but then they divided the circle into 8, 12, 120 and 240 parts, but not 60 parts. One reason may be that they believed the year consisted of 360 days. No one can say for sure. Most likely, 60 was recognized as being such a useful number because it can be divided exactly by so many other smaller numbers.

Though the base of 60 played such an important part in their number system, the Sumerians counted in tens by preference. They counted by tens (or decimally) to 60, which they called a Soss; then by 60's and the number over to 10 Sosses—or 600 —which they called a Ner; then to 6 Ner—or 3,600—which they called a Saru. Special symbols were used for the Ner and the Saru.

As you have seen, the Sexagesimal System had something in common with our present system, namely, place value. Just as 11 in our system (or notation) stands for $1 \times (10) + 1$, 111 for $1 \times (10)^2 + 10 + 1$, and 348 for $3 \times (10)^2 + 4 \times (10) + 8$, so these people wrote the equivalent of our 11 for $60 + 1$, 111 for $(60)^2 + 60 + 1$ and so on; but a number like 348 would really mean to them $3 \times (60)^2 + 4 \times (60) + 8$, that is, if you care to work it out, 11,048. Such a place system was to be of much help to them later when, under the Babylonians, fractional quantities were worked out something like our decimal fractions.

One thing in their system, however, was rather vague. Sometimes, a blank space meant a nought (zero), so that 8,4 might really mean $8 \times (60)^2 + 4$; that is, 28,804 instead of $8 \times (60) + 4$, or 484.

It is useful to remember that both the Sexagesimal System and place value remain with us today. The former is used in our division of hours and minutes, and in the division of the circle and degrees, while place value was most likely copied by the Greeks and Hindus through the communicating caravan routes through this part of the world, though, as we shall see later, the Arabs gave credit for this idea to the Hindus.

C. Unit Fractions

The Sumerians experienced some difficulty when they came to deal with fractions. To try to overcome this they wrote fractions as aliquot parts. An aliquot part, you may recall, is a fraction with a numerator of 1 (or unity); therefore this kind of fraction is known as a unit fraction. As an example, they would not write the fraction three-quarters as we do, but would break it up into the unit fractions of $\frac{1}{2} + \frac{1}{4}$. Similarly, $\frac{5}{8}$ would be written as $\frac{1}{2} + \frac{1}{8}$, and $\frac{7}{8}$ as $\frac{1}{2} + \frac{1}{4} + \frac{1}{8}$. Strangely enough, there was one exception to this rule, the fraction $\frac{2}{3}$. This was not broken up into aliquot parts but written as we would write it, as a proper fraction.

We shall hear more about unit fractions later when we read about the Egyptians, who developed them much further than the Sumerians or Babylonians.

D. Methods of Calculation

The Sumerians soon realized that multiplication is just repeated addition. They then drew up multiplication tables based on repeated addition. To multiply 60 by 8, they would write down eight 60's and add them up. They would then write the problem and answer on a clay tablet, which was kept for reference like a ready reckoner.

As early as 3500 B.C. they knew that the area of a rectangle is calculated by length multiplied by breadth. Later they found out that the ratio of the circumference of a circle to its diameter (what we call π) is always the same. They worked this out and estimated π as 3. This was quite near enough for their purposes, for if they wished to work out the contents of a cylindrical granary from this, they were not very worried if they had calculated slightly too much or too little.

They looked upon arithmetic as a very practical subject and were not concerned with anything more than the simple theories which would help them in their everyday lives. They could calculate how many bricks were required to build a wall to certain dimensions, and the answers they worked out were good enough, even if there were a few left over. In any case, several were likely to be broken or damaged during the construction.

When we come to the Babylonians, we find that they had extended mathematics considerably.

Just as the Sumerians had drawn up multiplication tables, so the Babylonians set down tables of reciprocals. You know from your arithmetic lessons that the reciprocal of any number, we will call it N, is $\frac{1}{N}$. Thus the reciprocal of 6 is $\frac{1}{6}$.

The reciprocals of the Babylonians, however, were written down as sexagesimal fractions, rather like our own decimal fractions, except that the base was to 60. If they wished to divide a number by 15, they would look up the reciprocal of 15, which is 4 in the sexagesimal notation, and multiply by that.

It was as though we wished to divide 80 by 4, when we would look up the reciprocal of 4, that is ·25 in our decimal notation, and multiply 80 by ·25.

Unfortunately, there was no decimal point or zero (that is, 0) until about 1,000 years later, so once again the exact meaning of a set of figures could only be understood from the context, but this should not be too difficult for us to realize when we see that our own logarithm tables are set down in a somewhat similar way.

Most reciprocals calculated to a base of 60 can be expressed as simple fractions, but in these tables there are gaps, for example, for $\frac{1}{7}$ and $\frac{1}{11}$. In such cases the Babylonians would find it necessary to fall back on their awkward method of division, and give the answer in their cumbersome unit fractions.

The Babylonians knew the relationship of the so-called Pythagoras theorem. They were aware that with the rectangle of sides in proportion of 3 to 4, or 5 to 12, the square on the diagonal is equal to the sum of the squares on the other two sides. But they knew this only for such cases, and where the diagonal was not a whole number they were unable to solve the problem.

Discoveries in recent years show that the Babylonians had started on algebra. While the Egyptians, as we shall see, could solve only linear equations, that is, equations of the first degree such as $\frac{1}{4}a+4=8$, the Babylonians of Hammurabi's day could handle quadratic equations (of the second degree, such as x^2, etc.), cubic equations (of the third degree), and even bi-quadratics (of the fourth degree). They had worked out the general rule for solving such equations, though their coefficients were small and fairly easy to manipulate; and while they had some knowledge of negative numbers, the negative root of a quadratic equation was always ignored.

Look at this example actually copied from a tablet about 1950 B.C.:

'An area A, consisting of the sum of 2 squares, is 1,000. The side of one square is $\frac{2}{3}$ of the side of the other square, diminished by 10. What are the sides of the square?'*

(This has been translated into English for us, of course.)

From your own knowledge of algebra, you will know that if we take $3x$ as the side of one square, $2x-10$ will be the side of the other. This gives us the equation:

$$(3x)^2+(2x-10)^2=1,000$$

which in turn gives:

$$13x^2-40x+100=1,000$$

The solution to this equation is $x=10$, or $x=-6{\cdot}923$, $x=10$ being the practical solution.

On the tablet the way to solve the problem is given, and also the right answer.

Other tablets show that these Babylonians were beginning to experiment with geometry. As a start they could inscribe squares in circles.

* From *Concise History of Mathematics*, by D. J. Struik (Bell & Sons).

When the Babylonians tried to solve their everyday problems, they often did so with a fairly near accuracy and, in the process, came across other things, ratios, fractions, particular solutions and shapes which they carefully noted. In this way they finally reached quite a high stage in their mathematics.

The ancient Greeks held the same opinion of them. Until the latest discoveries, within the last forty years or so, it was thought that the Greeks had been exaggerating. Now the archaeologists have shown us that the Greeks were right.

PART THREE—INTEREST IN ASTRONOMY

The Sumerian shepherd and desert wanderer was very impressed with the dawn, dusk, night and the changing moon. He knew that the seasons came round at regular intervals, and that crops and other things would reproduce only at certain times of the year, so that he felt, quite correctly, that his life was closely connected with the seasons. Finding plenty of time to study the stars, he saw that the heavens could foretell the times for sowing and other farm work, and felt that the stars, too, influenced his own life, just as some people feel today.

In this way he became interested in astronomy, which led on to astrology, or 'what the stars foretell'! But rather than individual horoscopes, these people were more interested in the future of their ruler, their country, their crops, and the possibility of floods or storms.

As early as 4000 B.C. attempts were made to find the number of months during which a season returned. This was done by the priests and scribes. The Sumerian priest noted how the moon changed at regular intervals, and decided to begin a new month with every new moon. He made up his year of twelve of these months, but when he found, as you would expect, that he had reached the end of his year a month ahead of the seasons, he slipped in an extra month to balance it up. As in Egypt, the

Mesopotamians did not number their years, but named each year after some important event, such as a great flood or some other calamity, or a great battle.

Until 700 B.C. our knowledge of Mesopotamian astronomy is rather vague, but from then onwards we know that accurate records were kept, and so thoroughly that the dates of eclipses and the appearance of comets could be calculated. The complete record of these things has been lost, but the oldest clay tablet which has been preserved was made in 586 B.C., and we know that the records went on for 360 years.

These records are of great use to us even today. They are the longest ever kept, for our records at Greenwich go back only just over 200 years. Fairly recently, modern astronomers referred to these records and were able to establish that the time of the earth's rotation is lengthening by 1/1,000th of a second every one hundred years!

Under the Chaldeans, about 600 to 500 B.C., astronomy made great progress. The five planets Mercury, Venus, Mars, Jupiter and Saturn were already known, and were considered most important in controlling the lives of men.

Read this prediction of the time:

'On the 14th of the month an eclipse will take place; misfortune for the lands of Elam and Syria, good fortune for the king; let the king be at ease. Venus will not be present, but I say to my lord there shall be an eclipse. Irasshe senior, servant to the king.'

This was followed later by:

'To the king my lord I have written: an eclipse will take place. This eclipse has taken place; it did not fail. This is a sign of peace for the king my lord.'*

The five planets mentioned above were considered as gods, plus the Sun and the Moon. Later it became the custom to sing

* Reprinted by permission of the publishers, Abelard-Schuman, Ltd. (New York), and Sidgwick and Jackson, Ltd. (London), from *The History of Astronomy*, by G. Abetti.

the praises of each god in turn, and in this way our present days originated, though other later nations changed the names as they came down to us.

About 500 B.C. a Chaldean astronomer called Nabu-Rimannu used the records mentioned above to work out the movements of the Sun and Moon. He recorded his findings, giving the movements of these two heavenly bodies daily, monthly and yearly, while he could foretell their eclipses and other important events in the skies.

This brilliant astronomer estimated the year as 365 days 6 hours 15 minutes and 41 seconds, which is the earliest known close approximation. When you consider that he was without even a crude telescope, to be only 26 minutes 55 seconds in error is a magnificent achievement. At the same time, it tells us of the high level of the mathematics of his day.

But one hundred years later another astronomer called Kidinnu made a similar group of tablets of even greater accuracy. Indeed, it is said that one of his measurements of heavenly movements is more accurate than figures in recent use by modern astronomers, because of the long records from which he worked. If these people had possessed some knowledge of geometry or trigonometry, they could have calculated their findings even more exactly.

The records of Nabu and Kidinnu came into the hands of the Greeks, who were able to make great use of them when they applied their geometry to the study of the skies. But we must never forget these two great Chaldeans, who must surely be the founders of the science of astronomy.

From what has been said in this section, you will appreciate that mathematics and astronomy were closely connected in early times, as well as in modern times. The need for a calendar, to calculate the seasons, for plotting out the land or for drainage, for navigation and, as we have seen, for astrology, meant that astronomy was given an important place in the studies of the priests and scribes.

They believed that their whole future was governed by the planets and the Sun and Moon, and were anxious to learn as much about their future as they could. Nor must we smile too readily at this belief. For the Sun and the Moon do play a considerable part in our lives, assisting our growth, affecting our health, regulating our tides, and controlling our food production among many other things.

Having spoken of the importance of astrology and astronomy to the Babylonians, we must mention something about the Zodiac.

Ancient peoples naturally thought that the sun travelled round the earth, and this apparent path was carefully mapped out. When the paths of the Moon and the other five planets were likewise worked out, it was seen that all seven of these bodies kept within a narrow strip of sky, which formed a great belt around the heavens. The Sun's apparent path (we now call it the ecliptic) was taken as the centre line of this belt, with limits of about 8° on either side of it.

Sighting from the earth, men would see the Sun against a certain group of stars (constellation), and they found that this background of stars changed regularly throughout the year. As— this was before they had worked it out more accurately—they considered the year to be of twelve months, each of thirty days, they divided this belt into twelve divisions (or constellations), and allotted 30° to each division.

They called this belt the Circle or the Girdle of Signs, and the arrangement itself may have taken place as early as 2800 B.C. What is most interesting from our point of view is that it is probable that the division of the circle into 360° had its origin in this Girdle of Signs.

As the Greeks adopted the Girdle, it is possible that they copied the number of degrees also, but we are not quite certain of this. They did not call the belt by its old name, but christened it the Zodiac.

You may wonder why they did this. Many of the constellations against which the sun could be seen were supposed to resemble animals, and zodiac in Greek means 'pertaining to animals'. For your interest, the first mention of the name, as such, that has so far been discovered was in the 4th century B.C., by the Greek philosopher Aristotle.

Some 2,000 years ago the sun could be seen against the constellation Aries (the Ram) at the vernal equinox (March 21st). Now, however, the sun is seen against the constellation of Pisces (the Fishes) at the beginning of spring. The reason that the sun appears to have fallen back in the Zodiac is that, just as a top wobbles as it spins, so does the earth. This wobbling, which was first explained by Sir Isaac Newton and is known as 'the precession of the equinoxes', causes several changes in calculations concerning the skies. As regards the Zodiac, the sun will continue to fall back very slowly, so that after 26,000 years it will be seen again as the ancients saw it, against Aries on the 21st March.

TYPICAL EXAMINATION QUESTIONS
BASED ON THIS CHAPTER

1. Give a short account of the contribution made by the Babylonians towards the formation of a calendar.

2. Give a description, with examples, of any number system (other than the one in common use) of which you have heard.

3. Write an account of the probable extent of early Babylonian mathematics.

4. Describe some of the impulses towards mathematics among the earliest civilizations, such as the Sumerian. In what ways did the social needs of the times influence its growth?

5. Where was mathematics studied before 1000 B.C.? Give a brief account of the work done and suggest reasons for it.

2: EGYPT

JUST as civilization developed alongside the two rivers in Mesopotamia, so it developed alongside the river Nile in Egypt. Once again, some means of recording numbers was found to be necessary, and with it some system of calculation.

Most of our knowledge of Egyptian mathematics comes to us from two sources. Both of these are ancient documents made of papyrus, which is the name of a reed used by the Egyptians to make a kind of paper. These documents were found, of course, in Egypt, and like the clay tablets of Mesopotamia, have been deciphered.

One of these documents is called the Rhind, or sometimes the Ahmes, Papyrus. It was written about 1650 B.C. and contains some 85 problems in mathematics. We shall discuss it more fully later. The other document is called the Moscow Papyrus, because it is now in Moscow. It was written about two centuries after the other one, and contains about 25 problems.

Although you will notice many similarities between Mesopotamian and Egyptian mathematics in this chapter, Egyptian mathematics had one essential difference; they were based entirely on 10's, that is, a decimal system. Just as, much later, the Romans used X, C, D, M, for each higher decimal unit, so the Egyptians used special signs for higher units.

The numbers of the Egyptians were recorded in two ways. These were by hieroglyphics, which, as you may know, is a kind of picture writing, or by a cursive (or flowing) writing called hieratic. Though there is no need for you to memorize the signs, here are the two systems set down for your general interest. Some of these numbers quoted are actually taken from the

Rhind Papyrus, and if you study them you will notice that they read from right to left, or the opposite way to our own system.

HIEROGLYPHIC NUMERALS

1	2	3	4	5	6	7	8	9	10	20	100

14	21	28	56

HIERATIC NUMERALS

1	2	3	4	5	6	7	8	9	10

PART TWO—UNIT FRACTIONS

In Egypt, too, the treatment of fractions gave great difficulty and, as in Mesopotamia, attempts were made to simplify the handling of fractions by reducing them to aliquot parts, again with the exception of the fraction $\frac{2}{3}$.

Though the most common fractions used by the Egyptians were $\frac{1}{2}$, $\frac{1}{4}$ and $\frac{1}{3}$, they developed their unit fractions much further. Tables were drawn up giving a complicated breaking up of fractions with a numerator of 2, or, as we say, fractions of the type $\frac{2}{n}$. This lengthy process was bound to slow up the development of their mathematics, and so of the other sciences which depend on this.

When you think of a fraction such as $\frac{2}{7}$ being written as:

$$\frac{1}{56}+\frac{1}{679}+\frac{1}{776} \qquad \text{or}$$

$$\frac{2}{43}=\frac{1}{22}+\frac{1}{946}$$

you will see what we mean.

One table of fractions dating from the 4th century A.D. gives unit fractional parts up to tenths from 1 to 9. That means to say that numbers from 1 to 9 were shown broken into $\frac{1}{2}$'s, $\frac{1}{3}$'s, $\frac{1}{4}$'s, $\frac{1}{5}$'s and so on to $\frac{1}{10}$'s. Then it gives the tens from 10 to 90, that is, 20, 30, 40, 50, etc., into the above aliquot parts. Next it gives the 100's to 900, and the 1,000's to 9,000.

Even here the process does not end. The table goes on to give the 11ths, 12ths, 13ths, 14ths, 15ths, 16ths and 17ths of the units from 11 to 17. If you would like two of their examples to help you to understand this, here they are:

$$\tfrac{1}{9} \text{ of } 50 = 5\tfrac{1}{2} + \tfrac{1}{18}$$
$$\tfrac{1}{11} \text{ of } 9 = \tfrac{1}{2} + \tfrac{1}{4} + \tfrac{1}{22} + \tfrac{1}{44}$$

Even if you find all of this difficult to follow, you will now understand more clearly that the question of fractions was one which caused the Egyptians much anxiety and work, for we do not know just how they arrived at these answers, unless they were the accumulated work of thousands of years arrived at mostly by trial and error.

PART THREE—MENSURATION

We have all heard of the Great Pyramids of Egypt and the fascinating stories which surround them. But one of the things we often overlook is the mathematical exactness with which they were built. The four sides, for instance, face directly north, south, east and west respectively. This may not impress you at first, but just stop to think for a moment how the Egyptians might have found direct north and east.

One method was probably by means of a pole and its shadow cast by the Sun (see sketch overleaf). Around the base of the pole a semi-circle could be drawn in the sand with a piece of rope. As you can see, the shadow of the tip of the pole would just touch the circle exactly at two points only, once before and once after noon. These points would be marked, and the angle

c

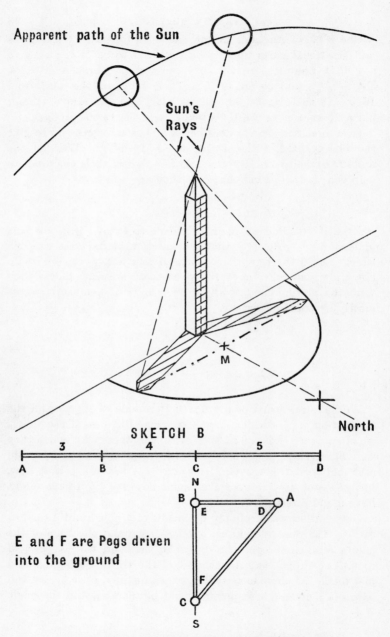

Apparent path of the Sun

Sun's Rays

M

North

SKETCH B

3   4   5

A   B   C   D

N

B   E   D   A

F

C

S

E and F are Pegs driven
into the ground

ONE METHOD OF FINDING NORTH AND EAST

between them bisected, perhaps by trial and error or by folding a rope which is the exact distance between the points into two parts, then marking where one end M comes along the straight line. This new point would indicate due north, and a line drawn from it to the centre of the pole would give a north-to-south line.

To obtain an east-to-west line, some authorities believe that the Egyptians used people called rope-fasteners. If this were so, three knots would be tied in a rope in the ratio of 3 : 4 : 5. If you refer to Sketch B you will see that ABCD is the rope, with knots at B and C. BC would be placed along the north-to-south line and pegged down at E and F. Piece AB would be pulled round peg E, and the other piece CD round peg F, until the ends A and D just touched. This point would be marked, so that the angle at E would be, of course, a right angle.

You will see that the Egyptians, too, knew of the so-called Pythagoras Theorem, namely, $B^2 + P^2 = H^2$. Like the Mesopotamians, also, they knew that 5, 12 and 13 would also give a right angle, but they were incapable of proving the theorem as you most likely can.

It is quite possible that they used the above method to set up square corners to their buildings, and in this respect you may like to know that the greatest angle error of the Great Pyramid is $12''$, or $\frac{1}{27000}$ of a right angle, while the largest error in the length of the sides is ·63 of an inch.

Another surprising fact regarding the Pyramids is that the sides and heights are in the ratio of 11 : 7, which hardly requires working out to see that the ratio of half the perimeter to the height is just $3\frac{1}{7}$.

From studies of the work which they have left behind, it is clear that the Egyptians had a good knowledge of mensuration. They had a rule for calculating the area of a triangle, which was $\frac{1}{2}(b \times h)$. They could calculate the area of a trapezium and the area of a circle, the latter by a formula, given on page 29, which makes the estimate of π as 3·1604. In point of fact, the Moscow Papyrus gives a formula for the area of the surface of a sphere which makes $\pi = 3·14$, within 0·01 of modern estimates.

Not all of their plane geometry was as accurate as this, for in dealing with the area of some rectilinear figures, the formulae they used appear to be incorrect if the texts of their work have been interpreted correctly.

In solid geometry, too, some of their formulae were not accurate. Rolls have been found showing ways of calculating how many bushels of grain there were in cylindrical granaries of varying depths and diameters, and in rectangular and other shaped ones As regards the rectangular containers, where they are defined by three lines, a, b, c, the answers given suggest that the formula used was:

$$a \times b \times (c + \tfrac{1}{2}c)$$

In modern form this is: $1\tfrac{1}{2}abc$, likewise incorrect.

At least one formula is astonishing. This is a formula for calculating the frustum of a square pyramid (the portion left when some part of the top is cut off parallel to the base).

It is: $\tfrac{1}{3}h(a^2 + ab + b^2)$

where a stands for the length of the base, b for the length of the top, and h the altitude. It has been said that this result has nothing to compare with it in the whole history of ancient mathematics, for its calculation involves a mathematical process (that of continuity) which was not developed until many centuries later. It is even believed that they could calculate the cubical content of a hemisphere, the formula for which was not discovered in Europe till some 3,000 years later.

The Egyptians were interested in mensuration and surveying mostly out of necessity. When they marked out their plots of land in the Nile valley, they knew that these marks would only last until the next flooding of the river, when they would be washed away again.

As a result the priests made a special study of surveying, and with all the practice they got, became quite accomplished in the science, so that they could carry a line in a level plane around all the bends of the River Nile for 700 miles, while about 1800 B.C. a great system of irrigation (canals and dykes) was effectively carried out.

In view of these numerous achievements you may wonder

why we call the Greeks the first real mathematicians. Mathematical knowledge in Egypt was confined to the priests and scribes, who were the only people who could write. The masons and carpenters and so on could not write and had to pass on their knowledge from mouth to mouth. The priests, in particular, jealously guarded their secrets and did all they could to withhold them from the other classes, so that they could maintain their tight grip on the ordinary people. They therefore left practically nothing of their methods of working out their problems.

Today we know quite a lot of what they could do, but we know so very little of just how they went about it.

PART FOUR—THE AHMES PAPYRUS

You may remember the names of the two Egyptian papyri from which we have learnt so much of that country's mathematics. One of these, the Ahmes Papyrus, we will discuss in more detail.

The papyrus is called this because it is the name of the Egyptian scribe who wrote it about 1650 B.C., and it is therefore one of the oldest manuscripts on papyrus in existence. But it is sometimes known as the Rhind Papyrus, because it was purchased in the middle of the 19th century by an Egyptologist (one who studies ancient Egypt) named Henry Rhind.

The papyrus, which is now in the British Museum in London, was deciphered, and in 1927 its contents were published. It is important to remember, however, that the work was intended as a practical handbook—something like a ready reckoner—to have by you, rather than as a textbook to educate the scholar, and it represents the accumulated knowledge of many centuries.

In the first part of the work Ahmes deals with unit fractions of the form $\frac{2}{2n+1}$ where n stands for all odd numbers from 5 to 49.* For example, Ahmes states that $\frac{2}{35}$ is the sum of:

* According to D. E. Smith, *History of Mathematics*. Some authorities state that it goes to 331.

$$\tfrac{1}{24}+\tfrac{1}{58}+\tfrac{1}{174}+\tfrac{1}{132}$$

You might like to work this out to see how near he was!

Ahmes merely records these results, for it is possible that they were worked out by earlier mathematicians, each of whom worked in his own way or by repeated trials. It is difficult to know just how these results were achieved, but in one case a method is suggested when Ahmes says that $\tfrac{2}{3}$ is the sum of $\tfrac{1}{2}$ and $\tfrac{1}{6}$, and adds that therefore $\tfrac{2}{3}$ of $\tfrac{1}{5}$ is equal to the sum of $\tfrac{1}{2}$ of $\tfrac{1}{5}$ and $\tfrac{1}{6}$ of $\tfrac{1}{5}$, which is really $\tfrac{1}{10}+\tfrac{1}{30}$.

When he has finished with unit fractions, the scribe goes on to deal with examples in arithmetic. When referring to multiplication, he seems to depend on repeated additions. If it is necessary to multiply, say, 15 by 13, he adds two 15's to get 30 (that is, 2×15). Next he would double this answer to get 60 (4×15). He would double this again to get 120 (8×15), and would then add them up in this way:

$$15+60+120 \quad \text{to get } 195.$$

This is an example of his method only, not one of his own examples. If you would like it in an algebraic manner, call the number x. Then by additions you will get x, $2x$, $4x$, $8x$, and by $x+4x+8x$ we get $13x$.

Ahmes has also set down some answers to problems involving division. These may have been worked out by repeated subtractions, but as he so rarely explains his methods we cannot be sure of this.

Next he solves some rather easy numerical equations. He sets this problem, 'heap', which we should call x, indicating in Egyptian a large number:

'Heap, its seventh, its whole, it makes nineteen.'

He is saying that the object of the problem is to find a number such that the sum of it and $\tfrac{1}{7}$ of it shall equal 19. He gives the answer: $16+\tfrac{1}{2}+\tfrac{1}{8}$. This is really what is now known as a linear equation of the type: $x+\dfrac{x}{7}=19$.

Another of his problems is not so simple to follow:

'Heap, together with its $\frac{1}{5}$ makes 21. What is it?'

Ahmes would multiply 1 and $\frac{1}{5}$ by 5, so that he had 5 and 1, making 6, which is too small. To find just how many times too small, he would divide 21 by 6, the result being $\frac{1}{2}$ and 3. Multiplying 5 by this result, he would get $17\frac{1}{2}$.

It is most interesting to know that Ahmes even had a rough idea of algebraic symbols, such as the unknown, plus and minus. In the arithmetical part of the papyrus he indicates the unknown by a symbol which stands for heap. Addition he sometimes represents by two legs walking forward, and subtraction by two legs walking backward, but, most astonishing of all, he indicates equality by this: ⋜

The last part of the manuscript is concerned with mensuration and some geometrical problems. He gives us some figures which represent the contents of barns, but we are unable to tell the exact shape of these so that we do not know how accurate his answers may be. We do know, however, that he used the formula stated on p. 26 for a figure of three linear dimensions.

Ahmes shows us how the Egyptians calculated the area of a circular field. He quotes a field of diameter 12, giving us no idea at all of what the 12 represents, and then states the result as

$$(d-\tfrac{1}{9}d)^2$$

where d is, of course, the diameter. We should call this

$$\tfrac{64}{81}d^2$$

and if you care to work out this formula you will find that the value of π becomes 3·1605, a result which is quite near for his times.

Finally, Ahmes gives the answers to some problems on the pyramid. These problems seemed very involved to us for some time, for it was difficult to understand what they were really about. It would seem that Ahmes was trying to find the ratio of some other dimensions which could not be easily measured, by means of measurements and facts obtainable from the outside of the pyramid. His method is similar to ours for finding the ratio of certain angles, as we do in trigonometry, and his figures agree closely to the dimensions of the pyramids as they are today.

From all this you can see that the examples of Egyptian mathematics in our possession are very practical and deal with numbers only. They were not interested in *why* the answer to a problem was so, only that it was. It is for this reason that we cannot refer to them, or the Mesopotamians, as the true founders of the science of mathematics.

Yet this does not mean that we must belittle the wonderful achievements that these people accomplished.

TYPICAL EXAMINATION QUESTIONS
BASED ON THIS CHAPTER

1. Write an essay based on the number system of the Egyptians.

2. Write an account of the Ahmes Papyrus.

3. Give an account of the typical problems in mathematics that interested the ancient Egyptians.

4. In what way did the social needs of the Egyptians influence the growth of their mathematics?

5. Where was mathematics studied before 1000 B.C.? Give some account of the work achieved, and suggest reasons for this.

3: IONIAN GREECE

PART ONE—HISTORICAL BACKGROUND

THE background for our story now moves to the other side of the Mediterranean Sea, to Greece, where some 3,000 years ago a race of primitive peoples descended from the middle of Europe and spread into the neighbouring countries.

In Greece itself these people settled down into communities, often cut off by the sea or by mountains, and thus they developed independently into what were called 'city states', rather like small countries. For hundreds of years these city states quarrelled and fought amongst one another, until, about 350 B.C., they were united into what was to become a great empire under a king called Alexander the Great.

Even before this time, however, the Greeks were a sturdy independent people with a keen interest in life. They had no large background of knowledge or science of their own, and, especially, no system of priests to keep them in ignorance. They were observant and curious and saw much good in the works of the Egyptians and Mesopotamians, but they did not copy it all. They realized, for instance, that the picture diagrams of the Egyptians were clumsy, but they grew interested in the alphabet of the Phœnician traders. Since this had no vowel sounds but contained a few letters for sounds not existing in Greek speech, they used these 'odd' letters for Greek vowels and so produced a complete alphabet. You see, they were open to knowledge.

Now everyday life in Greece was based on slavery, and the rich slave-owners enjoyed attending public meetings and listening to the public speakers. As time went on, they developed a method of argument (or reasoning) in an attempt to find the truth on any subject. They would start from simple facts already known, and by means of sound reasoning, carry the discussion on to its proper (or logical) conclusion, however unpleasant the answer might be to them.

As you may know, the greatest achievement of the Greeks in the field of mathematics was made in geometry. The word itself comes originally from two Greek words, 'geo', meaning earth, and 'metria', measurement; it therefore meant, in the first place, the same as our word 'surveying'. We have read that surveying was well developed in Egypt, and the name could have been translated from that country.

Starting from simple and fairly obvious truths, called axioms, the Greeks finally arrived at a great system of geometry by their sound methods of argument (or logical reasoning).

We have all heard of Euclid, and perhaps connect his name more than any other with the study of geometry. But in case

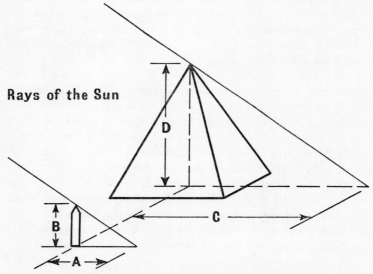

Rays of the Sun

How Thales measured the height of the Pyramid.
As A (the shadow of the pole) is to B (the height of the pole), so is C (the Pyramid's shadow plus half the base) to D (the height of the Pyramid). By measuring accurately A, B and C, it was a simple matter to calculate D.

PART TWO—THALES

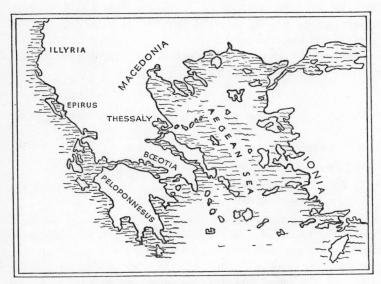

ANCIENT GREECE AND ASIA MINOR

you think that he was the first of the Greek mathematicians
you should know that this was not so. Now let us try to see,
then, who was a founder of this science.

If you look at the map above, you will see on the west coast
of what is called Asia Minor, the country of Ionia. Two
men originated from here who are usually given the title of
The Founders of Geometry. They are Thales, who lived about
640 to 550 B.C., and Pythagoras, about 582 to 510 B.C.

Thales was perhaps the first of the Ionian Greeks to make
a thorough study of mathematics, and to realize that it is closely
connected with astronomy and geometry as well as with numbers. But it is in his work of demonstrating the truth of a proposition (what is known as Demonstrative Geometry) that we
most remember him.

He was really a merchant, but he had some knowledge of engineering. He travelled widely, visiting Egypt among other places, and he was very impressed with the Pyramids. He was able to calculate the heights of these by the length of their shadows, and he probably did this by using his 5th theorem (below) and the shadow of a pole.

Here are the six propositions with which Thales is credited:

1. Any circle is bisected by its diameter.

2. The angles at the base of an isosceles triangle are equal.

3. When two lines intersect, the vertically opposite angles are equal.

4. An angle in a semicircle is a right angle.

5. The sides of similar triangles are proportional.

6. Two triangles are congruent if they have two angles and a corresponding side respectively equal.

Each one of these is very obvious to us now, but we must remember Thales because he was the first man to *prove* them. Until his time geometry consisted mostly of mensuration, measuring surfaces and solids, but the work of Thales made the subject a theoretical (or, as we say, abstract) study of lines, and for the first time we meet with a step by step (deductive) proof, as is now used in demonstrative geometry. From his time to the end of their ancient history, this kind of geometry was the chief part of Greek mathematics, and it is strange that they were the only nation to help its development for many centuries.

During his travels, Thales obtained from the Chaldeans a list of their observations on heavenly bodies. With this he calculated, as they had done before, when the next eclipse would occur, and he told the people of his native city, Miletus, when to expect it. He soon became famous when this came about in 585 B.C. But still more important was that he saw, and was not afraid to state, that the movements of the Sun and Moon were not the work of mysterious gods, but the result of fixed laws.

PART THREE—PYTHAGORAS

A. *The Pythagorean School*

Pythagoras is believed to have been a pupil of Thales. He was born at Samos on the island of that name off Ionia, and later travelled around the Mediterranean lands, gaining knowledge from the wise men of Phoenicia, Syria, Egypt and Babylonia. He eventually settled at the Greek city of Crotona in southern Italy about 529 B.C.

Here he started a centre of learning, and he divided those who attended for instruction into two groups, probationers (or learners), and Pythagoreans. The Pythagoreans formed themselves into a kind of secret society with the idea of sharing all things, and they were governed by a strict discipline. They were also pledged to keep their knowledge to themselves, and at least one of their number was murdered for disclosing a new discovery. The society became so powerful that it was eventually banned, and Pythagoras and many of his followers were subsequently slain.

Some of their discoveries were quite interesting and useful, but you may think that many of their beliefs were ridiculous. Again you must remember, however, that your background is so much advanced beyond that which they inherited, so that most of the things stated below were, in those days, considered very far-reaching.

B. *Geometry*

In plane geometry the Pythagoreans knew that the flat surface about a point can be filled with six equilateral triangles, four squares, or three regular hexagons. Pythagoras proved the proposition relating to the sum of the angles of a triangle and a few others. Though he is given credit for the theorem which bears his name, you have already learnt that the Egyptians used this at least 1,500 years before, while the Chinese knew of it about

100 years previously, and the Hindus were aware of it, too. Also, we are still in great doubt as to the method of demonstration Pythagoras used.

In solid geometry, the Pythagoreans called the sphere the most perfect of all solids. They knew that there were five regular solids which will lie exactly (or, to use the correct geometrical term, can be inscribed) in a sphere. The general name for these solids is polyhedra, but this is a name which does not appear in early Greek writings. Polyhedra are given special names according to the number of sides which make up the solid. So we have the tetrahedron, made up of four triangular sides; the hexahedron, a cube, made up of six sides; the octahedron of eight sides; the dodecahedron of twelve sides; and the icosahedron made up of twenty sides.

These were the five regular polyhedra of the Pythagoreans. Pythagoras most probably gained his knowledge of the cube, the tetrahedron and the octahedron from Egypt, but it is possible that the icosahedron and dodecahedron were developed in his own school.

One Greek writer called Plutarch says that Pythagoras stated that the earth was produced from the regular hexahedron, and believed that fire was the result of the tetrahedron, air came from the octahedron, water from the icosahedron, and the universe or heavenly sphere from the dodecahedron; probably the latter was given this honour because it was the last one to be discovered.

It is generally believed that Pythagoras did not construct these shapes as Euclid did later, though he and his followers knew that they could all be inscribed in a sphere. It is most likely that they handed on the study of these figures to some later school, where they were considered so important as to be known as 'Platonic Bodies' or 'Cosmic Figures'.

Pythagoras studied the properties of areas and volumes, and he was the first to prove that the circle contains a greater area than any plane figure with the same perimeter, while the sphere contains a greater volume than any other shape bounded by the same surface area.

We can conclude this section by saying that he made geometry a science by basing it on axioms (self-evident truths), postulates (assumptions), and definitions, and by setting down methods of proof.

C. *The Properties of Numbers*

Pythagoras was one of the first men to class all numbers as even or odd, but he gave the name of 'gnomon' to all odd numbers. Any odd number, which we call $2n+1$, was looked upon as the difference of two square numbers $(n+1)^2$ and n^2, or, to illustrate this, $(3+1)^2-3^2$, where $n=3$. He also stated that the sum of the gnomons from 1 to $2n+1$ was a square number, namely, $(n+1)^2$.

For example, if $n=4$, $2n+1=9$; while $(n+1)^2=(4+1)^2=25$. The sum of the gnomons from 1 to 9 is $(1+3+5+7+9)=25$, which agrees with his formula. You may like to try this for other values of n.

The square root of a square number was termed a Side by the Pythagoreans, while the product of two numbers was called a Plane, unless the product had no exact square root; when it was termed an Oblong. If three numbers were multiplied together, the answer was called a Solid Number, and if the three numbers were the same the product was called a Cube.

All of this, as you can see, referred to geometry, and we can follow this clearly by the remark of another famous Greek, Aristotle, who said that when a gnomon is put round a square the figure remains a square even though it is increased in dimensions. You may understand this better from the figure on p. 38.

Pythagoras was acquainted with what are known as triangular numbers, that is, the sum of a number of objects which are placed out in rows so that each row has one object less than the one below it, like this:

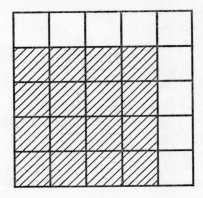

You can now see why they were called 'triangular' numbers. Added together they are $n+(n-1)+(n-2)+2+1$, where $n=5$ (the bottom row). The principle is the same no matter how large the triangle, providing n is always the number in the greatest row. You know this better as the arithmetic series $\frac{1}{2}n(n+1)$, where n is equal to the number of rows.

Pythagoras was very impressed by numbers and believed that they possessed different qualities. Many strange properties of numbers were supposedly discovered, and the numbers possessing them were given peculiar names.

Number 1, for instance, being the source of all numbers, stood for reason, 2 for opinion, and 4 for justice. In the properties of the number 5 was supposed to lie the secret of colour, 6 held the secret of cold, 7 the secret of health, while 8 held the secret of love. Just how they considered the mysterious properties of these numbers to be such, we will not bother about.

Pythagoras is believed to have made a useful investigation into music, and some believe he may even have begun the theory of music. By measuring the cords of the lyre, a musical instrument something like a small harp, he found that the fifth and eighth of a note can be produced on the same string by stopping at 2/3 and 1/2 its length respectively. In this and in other ways he started the idea of harmonic progressions, and is sometimes called the inventor of musical science.

Pythagoras was perhaps the most outstanding person in the history of ancient mathematics, and his teachings had a great influence not only on mathematics, but on the lives of most of the great thinkers of ancient Greece.

D. *The Greek Number System and Incommensurables*

From what you have read so far, you will have noticed two things. Firstly, the Greeks changed mathematics into an abstract science; that is to say, they worked out figures and constructions which were of little use in their everyday affairs. Secondly, they developed their geometry much more than their pure arithmetic.

One reason for these things is that going from one proposition to another, as they did with their plane figures, was in keeping with the fashionable interest in reasoned arguments (or logic). Another is that the Greek way of life was based on slavery, which meant that the rich people of the time found plenty of leisure hours to experiment with lines and shapes.

One of the chief reasons for the development of geometry under the Greeks, however, was the difficulties they experienced in using their awkward number system, for this was based on their alphabet. To understand this more clearly you might study the following, based on our own alphabet:

1	2	3	4	5	6	7	8	9	10	20	30	40	50	60	70	80	90
a	b	c	d	e	f	g	h	i	j	k	l	m	n	o	p	q	r

100	200	300	400	500	600	700	800	900
s	t	u	v	w	x	ψ	Ω	λ

Thus 'jg' would be 17, 'pf' would be 76, and 'uqc' 383.

But notice we have gone no further than 'x'. This is because there were only 24 letters in the Greek alphabet, so to be able to record numbers up to 999 the Greeks introduced the three signs you see for 700, 800, and 900. For 1,000 a bar was often placed to the left as:

/f, which, using the above symbolism, would be 6,000.

Although they counted decimally, there was no decimal place

D

system. Thus 'jg' or 'gj' would always be 17. Sometimes the Greeks used Egyptian unit fractions, sometimes Babylonian sexagesimal fractions, and sometimes even fractions resembling our own; but they never used decimal fractions, which would have helped them over many of the difficulties they encountered.

Such a method of numbering is very clumsy. The Greeks found it so, with the result that little progress was made with numbers —most of their calculations being done on the bead frame—so they branched out into geometry instead.

The Pythagoreans are credited with one other discovery of interest to us, namely, the difficulty of representing by whole numbers or proper fractions (called in modern terms, rational numbers) the diagonal of a square.

If a square is 1 in. by 1 in., then the square on the diagonal is 2 sq. in. But there is no whole number or proper fraction whose square is 2. We therefore say that the diagonal is an incommensurable, which means that its value is not expressible as an exact fraction.

This incommensurability, as it is called, put the Greeks to considerable trouble, for rational numbers, those which could be measured with a ruler divided into units, were the only numbers they recognized. After much valuable work in trying to solve the difficulty, they still found themselves in a dilemma. Either they must improve their number system to include these peculiar (irrational) numbers, or leave out measurement altogether from their geometry.

They chose the latter course. Instead of speaking of a line 4 units in length, or a triangle of base 3 units and altitude 4 units, or a figure 6 square units in area, they spoke of a line *ab*, a triangle *abc*, or a figure of length *ab* and breadth *cd*.

Nevertheless, they could do many clever things with their lines and figures, and many of the problems they were unable to solve with their number system they could solve by means of geometric construction. By tracings in sand the practical man might solve square roots, as you can see from the sketch, and it is known that they could solve some quadratic equations by means of their geometry.

Nowadays we speak of $\sqrt{2}$ or π as real numbers, and call them irrationals, and we work them out to whatever limits are necessary.

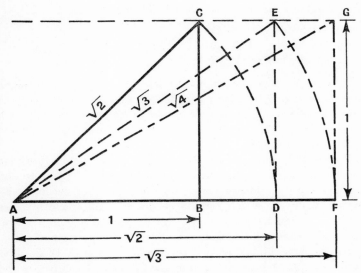

A Method of Finding the Square Root Geometrically.

If AB and BC are 1 unit each (inches, feet, yards, etc.) the diagonal AC $= \sqrt{2}$, because:

$AB^2 + BC^2 = AC^2$. Therefore $1 + 1 = (\sqrt{2})^2$, while $AC = \sqrt{2}$.
In Triangle ADE, $AD = \sqrt{2}$ and $DE = 1$.

Therefore the diagonal $AE = \sqrt{(\sqrt{2})^2 + 1} = \sqrt{2+1} = \sqrt{3}$.
This can be repeated indefinitely. Thus:

$AF = \sqrt{3}$ and the diagonal $AG = \sqrt{(\sqrt{3})^2 + 1} = \sqrt{4}$.

PART FOUR—THE THREE CLASSICAL PROBLEMS

Quite early in their history, the Greeks discovered that there were three problems which they could not solve exactly with only the compasses and an unmarked ruler, a condition that was generally insisted upon.

We do not know what suggested these problems at first, though there are several fanciful stories to explain their origin, but the problems are usually known now as the Three Classical Problems or the Three Problems of Antiquity. They were:

(a) Trisection of an angle.
(b) Duplication of the cube.
(c) Quadrature of the circle.

Now the meaning of each of these is (a) the dividing of any angle into three exactly similar parts; (b) the finding of the length of the side of a cube whose volume is exactly double that of a given cube; (c) the finding of a square whose area is equal to that of a given circle.

We are not going too deeply into the question, but there are three ways of attempting these problems. Firstly, by ruler and compasses only, which we now know is impossible; secondly, by means of curves which cannot be drawn with the compasses (known as higher plane curves); thirdly, by using minute quantities in involved calculations.

As we have hinted above, the geometricians of those days favoured only the use of an unmarked ruler and compasses and frowned upon any other means of solving these problems, though some Greeks did so by the second method.

One man called Hippias worked out a curve called the quadratrix with which it is possible to trisect any angle. Another called Menaechmus showed that the duplication of the cube could be solved by the intersection of two other curves called parabolas. A third noteworthy attempt was by Hippocrates, whose effort we will describe in more detail.

The important thing for this study is not the solving of the problems, but rather the many new discoveries and theorems which were made in the attempts, for in trying to overcome these Three Classical Problems the Greeks discovered much of their geometrical knowledge and obtained so many important results.

PART FIVE—HIPPOCRATES AND HIS WORK

Hippocrates of Chios is the man who was mentioned at the end of the last section, but he should not be confused with the other Hippocrates who is often regarded as the grandfather of medicine, though they lived roughly about the same time, 460 B.C.

The former Hippocrates was one of the many Greeks who attempted the Three Problems, and as a result of his efforts he is usually given the credit for three achievements. He compiled a book on the elements of mathematics, somewhat similar to, though not so thorough as, that which Euclid did on geometry; he found the area of certain lunes, which we shall discuss more fully; and he was able to find two mean proportionals between two given numbers, the result of his attempt to double the cube.

His work on the second achievement is still in existence, and it is about the only complete work we have of his time. It shows us the high standard of geometry which the Greeks of his day had reached, and, in particular, the sound logical deduction from one statement to another.

The work involves the finding of a square equal in area to a figure bounded by curved lines (in geometrical language, quadrating a curvi-linear figure). As you can see from the figure, he drew semi-circles on the sides of a right-angled isosceles triangle and proved that the two shaded lunes (or moons) are equal in area to that of the shaded triangle. Having arrived at a triangle, it was an easy matter to draw a square of exactly the same area.

This work of Hippocrates is noteworthy because it was one of the first successful attempts at quadrating a figure bounded by curved lines by means of the compasses and unmarked ruler only. Though we know that the method holds good for any right-angled triangle, Hippocrates knew it only for the isosceles right-angled triangle.

Hippocrates also did useful work on the geometry of the circle.

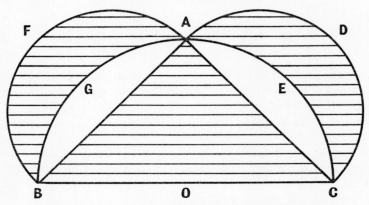

Hippocrates' method of finding the area of two lunes.

The square on BC=the square on AC+the square on AB. Therefore the area of the semi-circle on BC (BGAECO)=the area of the semi-circle on AC+the area of the semi-circle on AB. Take away the common parts, then:

The Area of Triangle ABC=the Sum of the Areas of the Lunes AECD and AGBF.

He proved that similar segments contain equal angles; and he may have stated that similar circles are to one another as the squares on their diameters, and that similar segments are as the squares of their chords. He is sometimes credited with being the first man to describe points and lines in geometry by means of letters.

But it is for his work on the area bounded by arcs that he is mostly remembered.

TYPICAL EXAMINATION QUESTIONS
BASED ON THIS CHAPTER

1. Describe how deductive geometry arose, and mention the parts played by some of the men who developed it in its early stages.

2. What were the three classical problems of antiquity? Show the importance of the attempts made to obtain their solutions.

3. Account for the difference between Egyptian geometry and the geometry of the Greeks. Give some idea of the extent of each.

4. Write an account of the life and work of Pythagoras.

5. Write an essay on the school of Pythagoras.

6. Write brief notes on the part played by Hippocrates in the development of Mathematics.

7. Give a short account of geometrical knowledge among the Egyptians and indicate the advances made by the Greeks.

8. Discuss the contribution the Greeks made to mathematics.

9. Write an essay on:
The three classical problems and their importance in the history of mathematics.

4: ALEXANDRIA

AT the beginning of the last chapter we mentioned that the Greeks were finally united under Alexander the Great. He was a young ruler, very interested in learning, who reigned from 336 B.C. to 323 B.C., and he won a vast empire in Egypt and what we now call the Middle East. At the mouth of the river Nile he built a city which was named after him, Alexandria, and it was here that Greek science continued for hundreds of years until the city was destroyed by the Mohammedans in A.D. 641.

For when Alexander died, his kingdom was divided among his three great generals. One of these called Ptolemy became ruler over Egypt, and he, also taking a great interest in learning, founded a magnificent university at Alexandria and did everything he could to attract to it all the best teachers of his time.

As Egypt was in a fairly central position in the Mediterranean world, the Greek mathematicians attracted to the university came into closer contact with the mathematics of Egypt and Mesopotamia. In addition, at Alexandria we meet with the professional mathematician for the first time, for the learned men there were paid to study and to teach, and could therefore spend all their time doing so.

In these circumstances Greek learning and science widened and developed, and mathematics, in particular, was looked upon as a separate subject and branched out as a study of its own, and the famous people that we are now going to read about were all connected in some way with the university of Alexandria.

46

PART TWO—EUCLID

It is a remarkable thing that we know so little about the life of a man who has influenced the teaching of geometry for centuries, and yet so much about his mind. Euclid may not have been a Greek at all for all we can prove. He may have been an Egyptian who came to Alexandria to learn, but it is believed that he studied at first in Athens in Greece. However, we do know that after a time Euclid was placed in charge of the mathematics department at Alexandria, and his influence on mathematics begins about 300 B.C.

No one will ever be more successful at writing a textbook than Euclid, for his work, called simply *Elements*, is still the basis for our school textbooks on deductive geometry, though we simplify them to suit our own particular needs.

The *Elements* is Euclid's greatest work, for it covers all the essential parts of the mathematics known at his time. But it has been so very successful, and is still so widely used, because of its simple yet logical order of problems and its methodical arrangement of definitions and axioms.

Before using a construction in a proof, Euclid demonstrated that the particular construction was possible and correct, while we sometimes assume the possibility and prove it later.

Also Euclid, of course, has no exercises of any kind, such as we find in our geometry books.

Here is an outline of the contents of the *Elements*:

I. Congruence, parallels, and the Pythagoras theorem

II. Algebraic identities, such as $(a+b)^2 = a^2 + 2ab + b^2$ which are treated geometrically; areas

III. Circles

IV. Inscribed and circumscribed polygons

V. Proportion, treated geometrically

VI. Similarity of polygons

VII, VIII, IX. Arithmetic, treated geometrically

X. Incommensurables

XI, XII, XIII. Solid geometry.

Though these are often referred to as books, they were really long pieces of papyrus or parchment rolled up and called volumes, a word which originated from the Latin 'to roll'.

The algebra that Euclid deals with in this work is set down, as suggested above, geometrically. An expression like $\sqrt{A}$, for instance, is introduced as the side of a square of area A, and a product AB as the area of a rectangle of sides A and B.

Not all the *Elements* represents his own work. Euclid used the work of those before him quite freely, though he probably discovered and proved, himself, many new things. But it is because this work contains all the mathematical knowledge that had accumulated for 200 years arranged in a clear and progressive way, that the name of Euclid will for ever mean almost the same thing as deductive geometry.

Euclid also wrote a work called the *Phaenomena*, which dealt with astronomy and contains 25 geometric propositions; a work called the *Data*, which was possibly about music; a work on the properties of light and vision (optics), on reflected light (a science known as catoptrics), and a few other works.

The result of all this was that men felt that geometry along these lines could go no further, and that any further advances would have to be made in some other direction, or, as we say, in some higher field of geometry. This proved to be the case.

PART THREE—ERATOSTHENES AND THE MEASURE-
MENT OF THE EARTH

Another great scholar at Alexandria some time after Euclid, about 270 to 190 B.C., was a man called Eratosthenes. He was greatly admired in his day, and some people think that he was given the nickname of Beta (which is the second letter of the

Greek alphabet and so stood for 2), because he was considered the second wisest man of Greece.

He was educated at Athens in Greece, and taught at Alexandria about 240 B.C., where he was made librarian of the university. He wrote a work on arithmetic now known as the 'Sieve', which was a means of separating all other numbers from primes. It was quite a simple method, for he wrote down all the odd numbers and then crossed out any that were multiples of those before them: for instance, 3 5 7 9̸ 11 13 1̸5̸ 17 19 2̸1̸ 23 2̸5̸, and so on. He really began the study of prime numbers, and it is interesting to add that no algebraic formula has yet been found for sorting out all prime numbers.

But Eratosthenes is best remembered for his scientific measurement of the earth, a science known as geodesy, and for this and his attempts at map making, he is called the first important geographer of ancient times.

Eratosthenes learned that the sun was exactly in the zenith (at 90°) at a place called Syene in Egypt (now known as Assouan) when it was 7 degrees 12 minutes south of the zenith at Alexandria. We do not quite know how he arrived at this angle, but it is thought that he may have used armillary spheres (a kind of globe made up of fixed circles), or a type of sundial known as the sca'phe. It was, however, common knowledge that on the day of the summer solstice, about June 21st, the sun's rays shone completely down the wells at Syene, whilst any object such as a pole or an obelisk (Cleopatra's Needle in London is one) would cast no shadow.

Eratosthenes knew that the distance between these two places was 5,000 stadia. Now the stadium was a unit of measurement used in those days which varied in length, for there was an Olympic (Grecian) stadium of 202¼ yards, and an Egyptian stadium of about 172¼ yards, but it is possible that Eratosthenes used the latter one.

Once again, just how he obtained this length we do not know, though attached to the university were men called 'pacers' whose job it was to pace out distances, and Eratosthenes, as librarian, would be able to consult their records whenever he wished.

With these facts before him, the ancient geographer concluded that Alexandria was 7° 12′ north of Syene, and bearing in mind that the complete angle was 360°, he realized that this measurement was exactly 1/50 of the circumference. You may appre-

How Eratosthenes measured the Earth

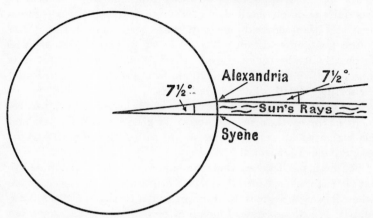

As the sun appeared to be 7½° south at Alexandria when exactly overhead at Syene, Eratosthenes assumed that Alexandria was 7½° north of Syene. He concluded that this was 1/50 of the earth's circumference, but he did not allow in his calculations for the difference in longitude of the two places, which would have lengthened the arc.

(Note: The sun is so far away from the earth that its beams are parallel for all practical considerations.)

ciate this more clearly from the figure. Since 1/50 of the earth's circumference was equal to 5,000 stadia, he concluded that the whole circumference was 50 × 5,000, that is, 250,000 stadia.

Now this would mean that each degree was equivalent to 649⅗ stadia, and since this great man was aware of the imperfection of his instruments, he thought it was quite permissible in the circumstances to allow 700 stadia for each degree.

You may have already realized that he did not take into consideration the difference in longitude of these two places, a difference which would have lengthened his arc. His figure of 700 stadia, then, was fairly reasonable, bearing in mind all the circumstances.

The rest of his calculation is easy to work out. Allowing 700 stadia to each degree would make the circumference of the earth 252,000 stadia. If Eratosthenes used the Egyptian stadium, which is most probable, his estimation of the diameter of the earth in our measure would be about 7,850 miles, which is only 50 miles less than the distance through the earth between the north and south poles, an amazing achievement for those times.

Eratosthenes also stated that the distance between the tropics was $\frac{11}{83}$ of the circumference, which makes the angle of the sun's apparent path (called, you remember, the ecliptic) 23° 51' 20", less than half a degree greater than it really is.

Another Greek called Plutarch wrote that Eratosthenes found the sun to be 804,000,000 stadia from the earth, and the moon 780,000 stadia. Using the Egyptian stadium again, this would make the sun's distance from the earth some 78,690,000 miles, and the distance of the moon about 76,300 miles.

We now know that the average distance of the sun from our planet is about 92,900,000 miles, and when we compare the effort of Eratosthenes with this, it is quite close for the crude instruments he had to use and the tremendous distance involved. As regards the distance of the moon, however, he was rather further out, for we now know this distance to be about 239,000 miles.

The work of Eratosthenes had a great effect on those who followed him, and consequently geographical knowledge increased quickly in the next 200 years.

PART FOUR—ARCHIMEDES

Almost every schoolboy has heard at some time of Archimedes and his many inventions. He came to study at Alexandria, and afterwards returned to his native Syracuse in Sicily to continue work in mathematics.

One report concerning him says that the Romans, who were trying to capture his country, were terrified of his 'engines of war', by means of which he kept them at bay for three years. On one occasion he is said to have set fire to Roman ships by means of the sun's rays and reflecting mirrors, but it is thought that, at least, he made the ships so unpleasant by this means that the soldiers were unable to stay aboard them.

Another story is the famous one of his proving that the king's crown was not made of pure gold by weighing the water displaced when the crown was immersed in a vessel, and of his exclaiming 'Eureka!' ('I have found it!') when the solution first came to him in his bath. This principle is now named after him and is to the effect that 'any body immersed in a fluid loses as much in weight as the weight of an equal volume of the fluid'.

He is usually considered the inventor of the Archimedean Screw, which is still sometimes used in Egypt for raising water. He possibly used this for the first time to remove water from the hold of a ship, and it consisted of a tube wound round a cylinder like a screw and open at both ends, its principle being that the inclination of the screw to its axis (or centre) must be greater than the slope of the axis to the horizontal, unless the screw is to be turned very quickly. Then, when one end is immersed in water and the tube rotated, the water will flow from the other end.

Archimedes, however, thought very little of these inventions which made him famous, for he considered them below the level of pure science, and often refused to set down any record of them.

Instead, he wrote on almost all the mathematical subjects known in his day, often in a disjointed way, so that it is not easy to write down the whole of his works and discoveries. Yet, judging by all that can be found out about him, his greatest work was in geometry, though we must never forget his other contributions to science.

On plane geometry, his works that are still in existence are: (a) the Measure of the Circle; (b) Quadrature of the Parabola (that is, finding a square equal in area to a parabola); (c) Spirals.

The Measure of the Circle contains three important propositions:

(i) The area of a circle is the same as that of a right-angled triangle with base equal to the circumference, and vertical height equal to the radius a, which really means: Area of circle $= \frac{1}{2}a(2\pi a)$.

(ii) The ratio of the area of a circle to the square on its diameter is approximately 11 : 14; that means:

$$\pi a^2 : 4a^2 :: 11 : 14$$

(iii) π is less than $3\frac{1}{7}$ but greater than $3\frac{10}{71}$.

These theorems are proved geometrically by Archimedes. You should, however, remember in particular that to demonstrate (ii) and (iii) he constructed regular polygons, often with as many as 96 sides, in and about a circle, calculated the perimeters of these polygons, and assumed the circumference of the circle to lie between the two answers. This method is sometimes called a method of exhaustions, and it can be compared with a modern method known as integration, as it might be explained in the first chapter of a book on advanced mathematics.

The work of Archimedes on the Quadrature of the Parabola contains 24 propositions, but these are too involved for discussion here, as is his work on Spirals, which contains 28 propositions.

On geometry in three dimensions, Archimedes wrote on:

(a) The Sphere and Cylinder.

(b) Conoids (solids based on sections of cones), and
Spheroids (solids generated by an ellipse).

Many of the rules he stated about the cylinder and cone were already known, but in his work on spheroids he stated that the sphere is four times as great as a cone of base equal to the largest circle (periphery of the sphere) and altitude equal to the radius. Also, just as a circle is equal to a triangle of base equivalent to the circumference and vertical height equivalent to the radius (see (i) above), so, he stated, a sphere is equal to a cone whose area of base is equal to the surface of the sphere and whose altitude is equal to the radius of the sphere.

Archimedes was very proud of his work called the Sand Reckoner, which is now lost. In this he tried to show how the grains of sand in the earth could be estimated by enlarging the method of numbering. In other words, he was one of the few Greeks who tried to improve the number system. He arranged numbers in octads or eighth powers of 10, 1–10^8 he called of the first order, 10^9–10^{16} of the second order, and so on. He extended the system to 10^{63} to calculate the number of grains in the solar system. But what we should remember especially, is that in this work he recognized the law that is the basis of our present logarithms, namely, $a^m \times a^n = a^{m+n}$, or, if you like, $x^2 \times x^4 = x^6$, etc.

Archimedes was unequalled for centuries in his work on the study of liquids at rest (a science known as hydrostatics), and he was a pioneer of specific gravity in particular, and of the centre of gravity of planes and solids. Indeed, it has been said that he represents the birthday of mathematical physics and Isaac Newton its coming of age.

Archimedes died at the capture of Syracuse by the Romans in 212 B.C. A great massacre followed the capture of the city, and as he was calmly working out some problem in the sand he was slain by a Roman soldier.

It can be truly said of him that he was one of the greatest mathematicians and physicists (one who studies physics) in all history.

PART FIVE—APOLLONIUS

The fourth great man of this period at Alexandria was Apollonius. We know that he was born at Perga in south Asia Minor about 260 B.C., and that he studied and taught at the university, but the rest of his life is unknown to us. He is remembered mostly for his work on conic sections, that is, the curves formed by cutting a cone in various ways, and his thorough work on these curves earned him the title of the 'Great Geometer'.

If you refer to the diagram (p. 56), you will see what the mathematician usually means when he refers to a cone; that is, a complete (or 'double') cone. You will also observe that by cutting the cone in four special ways, four different shapes will be formed, assuming that the axis of the cone is vertical.

The circle is formed by cutting the cone horizontally, the ellipse is formed by an oblique cutting plane right across the cone, the parabola when the cutting plane is parallel to the slant side, and the hyperbola when the cutting plane is vertical, or when the angle of the plane with the base is greater than the angle made by the slant side and the base. Notice, too, that the cutting plane which produces the hyperbola is the only plane which cuts both parts of the cone. In other words, the hyperbola is the only conic section which has two parts.

Conic sections had been known before the time of Apollonius, and some of their characteristics studied, but he was the first to investigate them in great detail. In particular he gave them the names of 'ellipse', 'parabola' and 'hyperbola', using these names to express a certain ratio concerning them, and he dealt so thoroughly with them that there was little left to add to his work by those who followed him. In fact, it was the standard work on conics till the end of the 16th century.

The complete work was made up of eight books, but the last one is lost, and of the remainder the first four are written in Greek, while the remaining three are Arab translations. Books I to IV are really an introduction to the subject and contain most of what was already known, though Apollonius, like Euclid in his *Elements*, arrived at his conclusions in a much more satisfactory way.

In Book I he shows how the three curves can be constructed from the same cone, using two lines at right angles to each other and co-ordinates (lines of reference). Except for the fact that he did not know of the directrix (a straight line used today to determine a conic) and the fact that the parabola had a focus (a point having a definite relation to a conic), the first three of his books contain most of the propositions that might be found in a modern book on this subject.

Books V to VII are mostly about his own discoveries, Book V dealing with what are known as normals (that is, perpendiculars)

E

CONIC SECTIONS

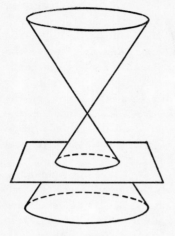

The Circle

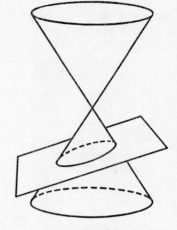

The Ellipse

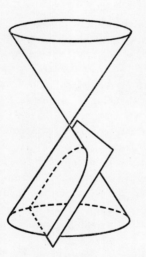

The Parabola

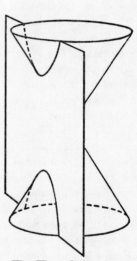

The Hyperbola
(Note that it has two parts.)

to curves, Book VI with the equality and similarity of these curves, and Book VII with diameters and figures drawn on these diameters.

Other works of Apollonius on geometry included plane loci (the paths described by moving points), the inscribing of the dodecahedron and icosahedron in a sphere, suggestions for the improvement of Euclid's elements, and a method for finding the value of π more accurately.

In arithmetic Apollonius improved on the number system of Archimedes, choosing 10^4 as a base. This number, known as the myriad, had been used as a base in the eastern world for hundreds of years, and became the base for some number systems in Europe also. Apollonius showed how multiplication by such numbers could be performed.

With his works Greek mathematics reached its highest point, for Apollonius and Euclid, whose works the former studied and used quite frequently in his own research, are two of the greatest figures in the field of geometry.

PART SIX—DIOPHANTUS

Diophantus is the last of the great Alexandrian mathematicians we shall discuss in detail, but before we do so we should just mention two famous astronomers who came before him. They are called Hipparchus and Ptolemy.

Hipparchus was a Greek who studied at Alexandria, then went to the island of Rhodes, in the Mediterranean, to follow his work. Unfortunately, as his own works have been lost, we can learn about them only from Ptolemy. To Hipparchus, however, is usually given the credit of being the first to study the trigonometrical properties of angles, and of drawing up a table of angles. He also made up a list of over 1,000 stars, which was a great achievement for those days.

A few years later Ptolemy put these findings of Hipparchus into a systematic order in a book called the *Almagest*, which once again became the standard textbook on astronomy till the days of the German Johann Kepler in the early 17th century.

Diophantus lived about the 3rd century B.C., and he wrote three works:

(a) A short essay on polygonal numbers (numbers in rows which form the shape of a polygon).

(b) A treatise on algebra.

(c) A work on porisms (a Greek proposition which could make a certain problem capable of many answers).

The most important of these for our study is (b), which is called *Arithmetica*, though it is about algebra. It is the earliest known work on this subject, but we do not say that Diophantus invented it, for, as we have read, the Mesopotamians and Egyptians were interested in algebra, but were hindered in this direction by a lack of symbols. Rather, we say that Diophantus developed it.

The *Arithmetica* consisted originally of thirteen books, only six of these being known to us now, and these are copies written in the 13th century. In this work Diophantus uses symbols and applies algebra to find the solutions to several problems which involve equations of the first and second degree, though the symbols he uses and those used by the writers in the 13th century are rather confusing. He solves one cubic equation (of the third degree), $x^3 - x = 4x^2 - 4$, as well as some cases of indeterminate equations (those which have more than one variable, such as $x - 2y = 4$, so called because there are an unlimited number of values which satisfy it).

In his notation Diophantus always used a symbol to represent the unknown, just as we use x, but he used generally only one symbol. This symbol is usually written as s (like the Greek letter sigma), the plural being ss, etc. The coefficients he uses are always numbers, which are written immediately after the quantity they multiply, as $x5$; and his powers, such as x^3, are likewise always numbers.

There is no sign for addition in this work, the quantities being placed alongside each other, but for subtraction the sign τ is used, and this symbol affects all those which follow it, just as does our minus outside a bracket. Diophantus states clearly that 'a subtraction multiplied by a subtraction gives an addition', so that he was aware of the rule for multiplying numbers with like signs.

The symbols mentioned above are really abbreviations for words, so that they are really contractions rather than true symbols. Nevertheless, the introduction of a contraction, instead of a word, to represent an unknown quantity meant a tremendous move forward in the development of algebra.

With his *Arithmetica*, Diophantus is ahead of the subject by many centuries, and it is very surprising that the Arabs, who were interested in algebra and were aware of his work, seemed to discard it. For the *Arithmetica* was not fully appreciated until its discovery in Europe about the 16th century, by which time the Arab influence was dying away.

TYPICAL EXAMINATION QUESTIONS
BASED ON THIS CHAPTER

1. 'Archimedes held that it was undesirable for a philosopher to apply the results of his science to any practical purpose.' Is this borne out by his work? Give reasons for your answer.

2. Write a short account of the attempt of Eratosthenes to find the size of the earth.

3. Write an essay on the life and work of Euclid.

4. Give the names of and indicate the parts played by mathematicians associated with the discovery or early development of:
    (a) The determination of the size of the earth.
    (b) Hydrostatics.
    (c) Conic sections.

5. Archimedes wrote on nearly all mathematical subjects. Give an account of his main achievements. Of which of these was he most proud?

6. Describe the contribution made to mathematics by:
   (a) Hippocrates.
   (b) Eratosthenes.
   (c) Diophantus.

7. Name the more important mathematicians of the Alexandrian schools and give the principal discoveries associated with each.

8. With what development of notation in mathematics do you associate Diophantus? Write a short account of his work in this connection.

Book Two

THE FOURTH TO THE SIXTEENTH CENTURIES

1 : THE ROMANS AND THEIR NUMERALS

In glancing through this short chapter, you may wonder why the Romans, who occupy such a large place in history, are dealt with so briefly here. The fact is, that the Romans contributed very little to the development of mathematics, or to any other science, but copied, with a few slight improvements here and there, what had gone before.

The Romans were a very practical people and were only interested in mathematics for what it could do for them, such as helping to extend their empire or to bring in wealth. They were good surveyors and builders, as you know, but most of their work in these directions was based on the mathematics they had obtained from other sources, especially from Alexandria.

One writer, called Geminus, although there is some doubt as to whether he was actually a Roman, is said to have divided mathematics into two groups, the pure group, which included arithmetic and geometry, and the applied group, such as mechanics, astronomy, geodesy (earth measurement), etc., and he is believed to have written a geometry on spirals and other figures.

There were several minor writers who made useful little contributions to the science on occasions, but none to compare with any of the great names you have seen in the two previous chapters. Julius Caesar, for instance, was quite a good astronomer, and he was responsible for some important surveys of his empire, as well as making an important contribution to the reform of the calendar, of which we shall hear more later.

We could not, however, dismiss the Romans from this work without some mention of their numerals. You know that these are really letters, I, V, X, L, C, D, M, and you may have read that these originated as hand signs. V is said to have come from the open hand with the fingers close together and the thumb out to the side, and X to have come from two crossed hands or one V on top of another.

Unfortunately, with the exception of C and M, which are generally accepted as being abbreviations for 'centum' (100) and 'mille' (1,000), the exact origin of the symbols is vague, though it is possible that they began as early Greek letters and underwent several changes.

Some authorities even believe that the V and X came from writing ten single strokes and crossing them off like this:

so that V would naturally be the top part of the X, and there is some support for this view on early Roman monuments, where 5 is sometimes indicated by an inverted V, namely, Λ.

The intermediate (or 'half-way') symbols of V, L (50), and D (500) were a useful means of representing numbers much more briefly than would otherwise be possible. So was the subtractive principle, that is, the idea of writing IX instead of VIIII for 9 and so on; yet even this idea was not new, for the Babylonians had sometimes used this method. The Romans were not even consistent with it, for sometimes they wrote XIX for 19, and sometimes IXX. CD for 400 was quite rare, and MCM for 1900, as you might see on some modern buildings, was never used. It is interesting to remember that the subtractive principle is still with us, as when we speak of the time as 'twenty to three' for 2.40, or a 'quarter to four' for 3.45.

The Romans also occasionally used the letter 'S' (short for 'semis'—half) for the fraction $\frac{1}{2}$, and they might therefore write SVC for $94\frac{1}{2}$ or SXC for $89\frac{1}{2}$; or even SIX for $8\frac{1}{2}$!

The Roman numerals were not really much of an improvement on previous methods, but they had one great advantage, that of being common to all countries under the vast Roman rule. It was this which made them so popular and long lasting. For the Roman methods of numbering and calculation continued long after Roman rule had died away, until, in fact, our present numerals were adopted generally in the 15th century.

TYPICAL EXAMINATION QUESTIONS
BASED ON THIS CHAPTER

1. What contribution, if any, did the Romans make to the development of mathematics? Give reasons for your answer.

2. Write an account of anything you have learned about the Roman numerals.

3. Did the Roman number system represent a great advance in numeration? Explain fully why this system persisted in Europe for so long.

2 : THE INFLUENCE OF INDIA

You may remember in your history lessons how the Roman Empire fell away as it was attacked by barbarians. With this decline, as we call it, we find that about A.D. 500 mathematical interest and investigation moved eastward to India, though was to return, once again, about 400 years later to Mesopotamia.

Like the Chinese, the Hindus, one of the Indian peoples, claim to be most ancient, but before A.D. 500 they had progressed very little in science. One of the earliest contributions of the Hindus was a series of books, no longer in existence, on astronomy known as the *Siddhantas*, which deal with certain figures and sexagesimal fractions, showing us that these people had contact, most likely by means of the ancient caravan routes, with Greece and Mesopotamia.

The results reached in these books were explained and developed by Hindu writers some time later, mostly in central and southern India, and the books of these Hindu mathematicians have been saved from about A.D. 500.

Arya-Bhata

One of the best known of these writers was Arya-Bhata, who lived in the early 6th century. His chief work is divided into four parts, three of which are on astronomy, while the fourth gives thirty-three rules in arithmetic, algebra and plane geometry.

This man is sometimes said to have begun algebra as we know it at school, though it is quite possible that he had seen some of the work of Diophantus. He deals with problems involving series, and linear and quadratic equations, and his solutions of many of these suggest that he was aware of the decimal system, for some of his arithmetic deals with numbers by tens up to 10^8. He also gives a rule for finding square roots, but some of his rules in mensuration are inaccurate, though he had a formula for calculating π which is equivalent to 3·1416.

Brahmagupta

A second great Hindu mathematician was Brahmagupta, who wrote a book in verse, two chapters of which are on arithmetic, algebra and geometry. The arithmetic includes integers (whole numbers), fractions, progressions, simple interest, the Rule of Three (the method of doing simple proportion), mensuration and some problems on simple plane geometry. As with Arya-Bhata, some of the mensuration is incorrect, particularly with regard to triangles.

The algebra he uses is often applied to astronomy, in fact he seems to be the first of the Hindu writers to attempt this. He gives the rules for negative numbers, devotes a chapter to quadratic equations, and forms a rule for solving quadratic equations of the type: $x^2 + px + q = 0$. He also writes on simple simultaneous equations, and solves some indeterminate equations (those, you may remember, such as $3x + 2y = 22$ which may have any number of values of x with corresponding values of y). For π he uses 3 as a 'practical value' and $\sqrt{10}$ as a 'neat value'.

After his time mathematics appears to fade out in northern India, probably due to a change of native rulers, but progress was made in southern India some 200 years later when the writings of the third of these Hindu mathematicians attracted attention.

Mahavira

Mahavira, who lived about A.D. 850, probably knew of the work of Brahmagupta, which was considered a standard work, for he tried to improve on the mathematics known in his day. His work consists of nine chapters, and names the operations of

addition, subtraction, squaring, square root, etc., and negatives
and zero, one of the earliest works in which the latter is mentioned. He writes of the law of zero:

'A number multiplied by zero is zero, and that number remains
unchanged when it is divided by, combined with, or diminished
by zero.'

His rule for division by fractions is worthy of note. It says:

'After making the denominator of the divisor its numerator
(and vice versa), the operation to be conducted then is as in
multiplication (of fractions).'

It is rather surprising that this rule, which was used in the
East, did not appear in Europe till the 16th century.

Mahavira deals also with quadratic and some other equations,
as well as with mensuration, though in the latter he makes
similar mistakes to those of Brahmagupta; for π he likewise
uses $\sqrt{10}$, an approximation which is found quite useful even
today, particularly where π^2 is involved. Of these three Hindus,
Mahavira, apart from the fact that he wrote more than the other
two, is the most outstanding.

Bhaskara

One other important Hindu mathematician must be mentioned, though he lived some 300 years later—about A.D. 1100.
Bhaskara the Learned, as he was called, studied at Ujjain in
central India, and he wrote on astronomy, arithmetic, mensuration and algebra. His best known work, called *Lilavati*, is mostly
about arithmetic and mensuration, and includes operations with
integers and fractions, interest, series, a little algebra and permutations (the possible ways in which a given number of things
can be arranged—see p. 121), and ratio, particularly the Rule
of Three.

But of more importance to us is the fact that it is the earliest
known work which contains the decimal system of numbering
in Hindu numerals, for though earlier writers showed that they
were vaguely aware of such a system, in Bhaskara's work it is
the basis of a well-established and consistent system.

Furthermore, a zero is used freely, and rules governing its use are set down. In our modern language Bhaskara says that a (any number)$-0=a$, while $a\times0=0$; but he was rather confused about $a\div0$, which he called an infinite quantity without explanation. We shall have more to say about this recognition and use of zero in the next section.

Bhaskara also wrote on algebra, particularly directed numbers (positives and negatives that are measured geometrically), on negatives, which he shows by means of a dot over the figure and calls them a 'debt' or 'loss', and unknown quantities, which he calls colours. A large part of the work is taken up by simple and quadratic equations, and these are dealt with in a much more straightforward way than by any of the other Hindu writers before him.

PART TWO—ZERO, AND DECIMAL PLACE NOTATION

It is not intended, in this section, to go into the origin and development of Hindu numerals (or figures). In fact, the origin of the symbols is probably buried for ever in the dim mists of early history. They may have begun as definite symbols, or as the initial letters of the numbers they represent (such as 't' for 2, 'f' for 4), or merely copied from symbols from some other country.

It is quite possible that in early Hindu systems, for there were more than one, additional symbols were used for numbers from 20 to 90, and for 100 and multiples of 100.

However, about the 8th century A.D. a set of numerals known as the Devanagari numerals appeared. These were different from all others before them, because they were based on a place value.

DEVANGARI NUMERALS

𝟏	𝟐	𝟑	𝟒	𝟓	𝟔	𝟕	𝟖	𝟗	𝟎
1	2	3	4	5	6	7	8	9	0

You see them written above, and it is quite easy to recognize the likeness between them and our own numbers, and in the next chapter we shall try to tell the story of the change from the upper row to the lower one. For the present, we shall discuss the symbol at the extreme right, for you may never have realized before how important 'nothing' really is!

The Introduction of Zero

It has been said that the introduction of zero as a definite part of a number system marks one of the most important developments in the whole history of mathematics. You may be so familiar with '0' that you find this difficult to understand, but if you have read through carefully the chapter on Mesopotamia, you may appreciate the statement above a little more clearly. How could we write a number like 5,070 without a zero? It might be written as 5, 7, but then it might easily be mistaken for 57 or 507, and working out ordinary arithmetical operations with such a method would lead to all kinds of difficulties.

Now we have coupled zero with the names of Mahavira and Bhaskara, but the idea of zero came long before these Hindus, for we have seen that a blank space in the Babylonian sexagesimal system often indicated a nought, but it was rarely used in the terminal (or end) position, and it was not by any means as important then as it is today.

The origin of zero is very obscure, just, as we have read, as is the origin of our other nine symbols. It may have begun as a small circle, being the abbreviation of a Greek word meaning 'nothing', or as a dot in a blank space. All we know is that a zero appeared in Hindu works in the 9th century, and that it must have been in use some time before that.

The Hindu merchants with their problems involving trade, taxation, interest and so on, as well as the mathematicians, who were often connected with trade in one way or another, felt the need for a zero, and it appeared. Though why they should have introduced it, and not the great mathematicians mentioned in previous chapters, no one can say.

Most probably there was no idea in the first place of using it to indicate a number, for the idea of '0' as a number can be confusing to us even now, if we think about it long enough; it merely denoted, as thousands of years before, an empty space. The much more important idea of using zero as a number probably grew naturally from the use of the zero symbol with those of the other numbers.

Once '0' or 'sunya' as the Hindus called it was introduced as a number, calculations could be performed as easily on a black board, using a cane pen and white paint, or on a table covered with coloured flour, as on the bead frame which had always been the custom. Furthermore, though large numbers were not used very often, they could be multiplied almost indefinitely, whereas on a bead frame of four columns you can only indicate as many thousands as the number of beads or counters that you can get on the thousands column. In addition to this, with zero as a part of a system of numbers the idea of negatives, -10 and so on, is much more clearly understood.

It is the use of zero which makes our numbers so easy to handle, and without it our present system of numeration would be little better than previous ones.

Decimal Place Notation

The second great contribution of the Hindus was that of a decimal place notation. We have already met with a decimal system when we were discussing the Egyptians and the Greeks, and it really means a system based on tens, so that 25 is really $2(10)+5$, and so on. We have likewise met with the place position, as in Babylonia, where ⟨⟨⟩⟩ would mean $2(60)+2$, or 122.

Now this second great step forward by the Hindus was a combination of both these systems into a decimal place position, so that numbering was by tens, and each figure from 1 to 9 had a second value according to its position, so that 5 could be 50, 500, 5,000, etc., according to the number of noughts or other figures after it.

F

The Hindu numbers suited this idea perfectly, for they were what are called single code symbols, unlike the Roman numerals when 8 has to be written as VIII, and 9 as IX. This single code system was most convenient when numbers had to be written down quickly, and was of even greater importance when written calculations were performed.

The earliest known use of numerals in a decimal place notation is on a plate of about A.D. 595 which has the figures 346 inscribed on it, but it is thought that long before this the Hindus were expressing large numbers by means of words or abbreviations arranged according to a place value notation, such as 3hun 7ten 5un, for 375, but there were so many variations and so little evidence, that we do not know this for certain.

We can only emphasize once again that the introduction of zero and the use of a decimal place notation really set mathematics free, and makes our present system, which is based on these things, the most useful number system in the world, though we must not think that it has no inconsistencies or disadvantages. For many of the names of our numbers, eleven, twelve, thirteen, are not consistent, some of the symbols can easily be confused, while some people would really prefer the base to be changed to twelve. These things, however, belong really to some other book.

TYPICAL EXAMINATION QUESTIONS
BASED ON THIS CHAPTER

1. Name any Hindus who wrote on mathematics and give a general indication of their particular contributions.

2. What is meant by a decimal place system of numerals? Where did our present system originate? Give reasons for your answer.

3. Why was the introduction of zero of such great importance in the history of mathematics? Write a short account of its origin and development.

4. Describe the contributions to mathematical knowledge made by the Hindus.

3: THE CONTRIBUTION OF THE ARABS

PART ONE—HOW THE ARABS OBTAINED THEIR
KNOWLEDGE

DURING the 6th century A.D., in what we now call Saudi-Arabia, a child called Mohammed was born. He spent most of his life in the city of Mecca, and after much grave contemplation, he began there a new religious teaching, called Islam, much as Christ had done in Palestine six hundred years before.

Arabia was not governed by the Romans, but was inhabited by wild tribes, yet the teachings of Mohammed, sometimes called Mahomet, changed these people into a united nation, and when their new spiritual leader announced that he was going to spread his new religion by force if necessary, his followers flocked to him, became powerful, conquered a large part of the known world, and became enemies of the Christian world for eight hundred years.

The Moslems, as they are called, were then a warlike people, and being so opposed to Christianity, when they swept across North Africa (you can see the extent of their conquests from the map) they destroyed Alexandria and set fire to the university there with its thousands of valuable rolls. Some people argue that this was a mixed blessing, in other words, it did both harm and good. For with the destruction of this great accumulation of learning much useful knowledge was lost to mankind, yet at the same time, this wanton destruction cleared the way for new ideas, enabled them to receive more attention than otherwise, and so helped them to develop more quickly.

Do not think that the Arabs were not interested in science. On the contrary, we come back to Mesopotamia, for there, in Bagdad, the centre of this great empire grew, and under the

73

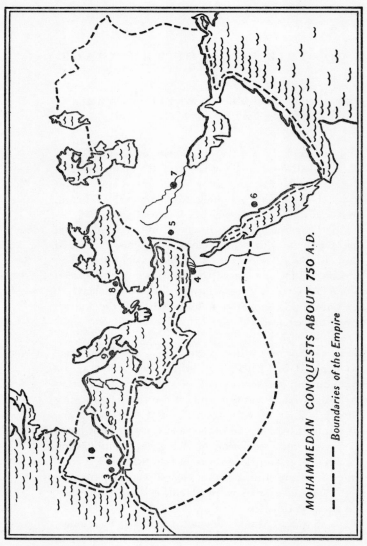

MOHAMMEDAN CONQUESTS ABOUT 750 A.D.

– – – – Boundaries of the Empire

Seats of Learning

1. Toledo (university).
2. Cordova (university).
3. Seville.
4. Alexandria.
        5. Damascus.
        6. Mecca.
        7. Bagdad (university).
        8. Constantinople.
9. Salerno (12th-13th centuries).

influence of its rulers, called caliphs, the city became a centre of learning also, rather like the one Alexandria had been.

Now much of the learning of the Arabs at Bagdad and the other important cities of the Moslem world was obtained in the first place from Greek and Jewish doctors who attended the caliphs, for when the Arabs began to settle in towns, adopting a very different life from their previous nomadic existence, they found themselves vulnerable to many diseases which they had not known before. Therefore, as the Greeks and Jews were the most advanced peoples in the science of medicine, their doctors were encouraged to settle in Bagdad and other cities.

It was soon realized that the knowledge of these doctors in other branches of learning was also much more advanced than that of the Arabs, so these doctors were often allowed to teach Arab children as well as advise on the sick. As these doctors had obtained their knowledge in the first place from Greek books, many of these were translated into Arabic, particularly in the reign of Haroun-al-Raschid, about A.D. 800, and of his son, Al Mamun, who reigned from A.D. 809-833. Al Mamun even sent special commissions to the Greek city of Constantinople (now known as Istanbul) and to India to get copies of as many scientific manuscripts as possible.

Indeed, this was the most important contribution of the Arabs to the history of mathematics. Clerks from Syria, masquerading as the caliph's doctors at first to avoid ill feeling on the part of the people, were engaged to translate the works of Euclid, Archimedes, Apollonius, Ptolemy and others, as well as the works of Indian scholars. In many cases these translations are our only means of knowing of the achievements of these men, for most of their original works or the Greek copies of them are now either lost or were destroyed in the sack of Alexandria.

We say, therefore, that the Arabs were transmitters (or if you like, 'passers-on') of scientific knowledge, especially mathematics, rather than originators. Yet we in Europe owe them a great debt and should pay them due tribute for preserving, in many cases, the only translations of the important Greek works, knowledge which would otherwise have been lost to all mankind.

The Arabs, of course, traded quite freely with India, and so obtained some knowledge of the works of the Hindu writers we have mentioned even as early as A.D. 750, but it was not until about A.D. 820 under Al Mamun that these things were closely studied. After that time the arithmetic and algebra of the Hindus was mostly copied by the Arabs, and was used by them in their own works.

PART TWO—ALKARISMI AND THE DECIMAL PLACE SYSTEM

It has already been said that the great interest in learning by the caliphs resulted in Arabic interest in the sciences. This was particularly so in regard to mathematics and astronomy, and just before A.D. 800 an Arab scholar translated the *Siddhantas*, which was mentioned in the previous chapter, from the Hindu.

He was followed by another Arab, whom we will call Alkarismi for short, who wrote books on mathematics and astronomy also. One of these was a small book, written about A.D. 825, which explained the use of the Hindu numerals. The book is now lost, but there is still in existence a Latin translation of it, written in the 12th century and called *Liber Algorismi de Numero Indorum*, or, as you would no doubt prefer it, *The Book of al-Khowarazmi on Hindu Number*, 'Algorismus' being the Latin interpretation of what we are calling 'Alkarismi'.

The title of this book gave the name of 'algorithm' to this new kind of arithmetic, based upon what are often called the Hindu-Arabic numerals. It is of great importance to us in this work, for it was by means of this book that the Hindu system, with its vital zero and decimal place position, eventually came to Europe.

This does not necessarily mean that the Arabs were not acquainted with the system before this book was written, for it probably passed along the caravan routes with the traders before this time, but it was the first important work to use the system and to explain it.

As you can see from the table below, the Eastern Arabs, as we call them, simplified a little the numerals of the Hindus, and as these numerals moved westward, they were simplified again by the Western Arabs, when they became known as Gobar numerals. The Arabs still use a modified form of the Eastern numerals, but our present figures are derived from the Gobar numerals, as we shall see in the next chapter.

Devanagari	१	२	३	४	५	६	७	८	९	०
Eastern Arabic	١	٢	٣	٤	٥	٦	٧	٨	٩	٠
Gobar	١	٢	٣	٤	٥	٦	٧	٨	٩	٠
Modern Arabic	١	٢	٣	٤	٥	٦	٧	٨	٩	٠
	1	2	3	4	5	6	7	8	9	0

Alkarismi also wrote another important work called, for short, *Al jabr*, which meant 'the science of reduction and cancellation', probably trying to convey the 'science of equations'. This also became known in Europe through a Latin translation, and the word 'al jabr', which originally applied to positives and negatives, eventually became 'algebra', and was applied to the science of equations.

This al jabr of Alkarismi deals with linear and quadratic equations, but not quite as we do today, for much of it is done geometrically. This work and others of his, which include astronomical and trigonometrical tables with sines and tangents, were chiefly practical rather than theoretical. They were also translated into Latin, and are quite important, for they were the chief means by which the Arabic algebra as well as the Hindu numerals came to Western Europe, and so to us.

TYPICAL EXAMINATION QUESTIONS
BASED ON THIS CHAPTER

1. Who was one of the most outstanding of the Arab writers? What were his chief contributions to the development of mathematics?

2. Estimate the part played by the Arabs in the development and transmission of mathematical knowledge.

3. Give an account of the main contributions made to mathematics by the Arabs in the 9th and 10th centuries. From what sources did they get their knowledge?

4. Write an essay on the contribution of the Arabs to the development of mathematical thought.

5. Write an essay on the Hindu-Arabic numerals.

6. Write a brief account of the part played by the Arabs in the history of mathematics.

4: THE INTRODUCTION OF THE ARABIC
SYSTEM INTO EUROPE

PART ONE—THE IMPORTANCE OF ITALIAN TRADE

WE have now to see how this new system of numerals found its
way into Europe. You will remember the Crusades, or Wars of
the Cross, which took place in the Middle Ages. From all over
Europe soldiers came to the Mediterranean on their way to
Palestine to try to free the Holy Land from the Turks. These
armies needed provisions and extra equipment, as well as trans-
portation across the Mediterranean Sea, and as they usually
crossed Europe to Italy, they brought great trade to the ports
of that country, such as Venice and Genoa.

As a result of this trade, these cities and others in Italy grew
into important trading centres. From Venice galleys set out for
the eastern Mediterranean to bring back the valuable spices,
silks and other things which had arrived there from India and
China usually by the long overland routes, while Florence also
carried on a thriving trade between the Arabs and Europe.

So rich was this trade, that Venice became one of the most
magnificent cities in Europe. She became what is known as a
'city state', for her merchants grew so wealthy and powerful
that they ruled over the city themselves by means of a kind of
committee or council. The other cities mentioned, Genoa and
Florence, as well as Pisa and Milan, also prospered greatly.

As we have seen before in history, this great trade made necessary an enormous amount of record keeping, so that the Italian
merchants were naturally interested in methods of recording
numbers and accounts, and in working out these things.

Calculating, in particular, was often a long process, for reckoning was done either on a kind of bead frame known as an abacus

(see p. 157), or by means of counters or discs on a squared table, and the results achieved were set down in Roman numerals, for the difficulty of handling these figures without any mechanical aid, such as is necessary in multiplication and division problems, had been obvious for centuries.

Our next step is to discuss an important link between the Arab and Italian mathematicians.

PART TWO—LEONARDO FIBONACCI

In view of this great volume of Italian trade in the Middle Ages, large warehouses were set up in most of the coastal towns around the Mediterranean where goods could be stored, loans obtained and debts could be paid. In charge of a warehouse in Barbary, on the north coast of Africa, was a man with a son called Leonardo. This boy was taught by the teachers available, mostly Arabs, to whom he appears to have given considerable trouble. As he grew older, however, he travelled around the Mediterranean countries, and being very interested in mathematics, he took especial notice of the different number systems that were in use.

He eventually came to the conclusion that none of these methods could compare with the so-called Hindu-Arabic system that he had learned in Barbary, and on his return to Italy, Leonardo of Pisa (as he was then called), or Leonardo Fibonacci (the name by which he is now more commonly referred to), wrote a book on this system of numerals in 1228.

This book, entitled *Liber Abaci*, meaning roughly, the Book of Reckoning, is important to us because it was the first systematic introduction into Europe of the decimal place notation, and in it Fibonacci explained the Arabic method of numbering and its advantages over the Roman system. It consisted of fifteen chapters, mostly on the processes of arithmetic, but included some elementary algebra, showing how to solve some simple and quadratic equations. As regards the symbols themselves, they were not entirely new to Europe, some acquaintance with them having been made through Spain and by means of Arabic traders, but in the *Liber Abaci* Leonardo explains not only the symbols but the whole decimal system.

The work was not very popular for some time. Fibonacci had not been educated by his own countrymen, and Italian professors belittled his efforts because of this, while as the Arabs were opposed to Christianity, their figures were called 'infidel numbers'. One order of 1259 distinctly stated that the bankers of Florence must not use them at all, though this was not done entirely out of prejudice. Everyone was so familiar with the Roman figures, and they were so difficult to alter, that fradulently changing them was almost impossible, which could not be said of the 'infidel ciphers' which were not, as yet, fully understood by everyone. But gradually, during the next century or two, the merchants and business houses saw the great advantages of the new system, and slowly adopted it for their commercial dealings.

Leonardo of Pisa wrote three other works. One of them, which we will call *Practical Geometry*, deals with the trigonometry of the Arabs, and he applies this to surveying. The other two books are on algebra. One of these deals with indeterminate equations, such as $x^2 - y^2 = z^2$, and he shows great ability in handling these. It also deals with series, in which Fibonacci was particularly interested, for it is said that he used to play with them for fun. Indeed, one series, namely:

$$0, \ 1, \ \frac{1}{2}, \ \frac{2}{4}, \ \frac{3}{8}, \ \frac{5}{16}, \ \frac{8}{32}, \ \frac{13}{64}, \ \frac{21}{128}, \ \text{etc.}$$

is actually named after him, and has a modern application in the laws of heredity (the passing on of certain characteristics from parents to children).

In the third book Fibonacci attempts to solve some cubic equations with considerable success, though his methods indicate that he may have had some contact with the mathematics of India or China in respect of these. In these works, too, he introduces occasionally letters for algebraical symbols, instead of writing out everything in full as was the custom in his day.

Fibonacci was well in advance of most of the so-called learned men of his day, for they found it very difficult to follow his clever methods. With these two great advancements, the introduction of the decimal place system and his elucidation of algebra, much of the latter being also translated from the Arabs, he is considered to be the most outstanding mathematician of the whole Middle Ages.

TYPICAL EXAMINATION QUESTIONS
BASED ON THIS CHAPTER

1. Describe briefly the influence on the growth of mathematics of commerce in the Middle Ages.

2. Write a short account of the influence on mathematics of trade and commerce between Italy and the East in the Middle Ages.

3. Indicate the contribution made by Fibonacci in the development of mathematics.

4. How have commerce and arithmetic influenced each other?

5: THE DEVELOPMENT OF ELEMENTARY ARITHMETIC

PART ONE—THE GROWTH OF THE NEW SYSTEM IN EUROPE

MOST calculations after the time of the Romans and up to the 16th century were performed on the bead frame, or abacus, and recorded by means of the Roman numerals. You can easily understand why this was so. How would you like to work out

$$MMCCCXXVIII \div XXIV$$

without using our own numerals? Such a sum without an abacus would give several difficulties, as would problems involving multiplication and subtraction, the processes being rather tedious. On the next page you can see how a comparatively easy sum might have to be worked out with the aid of an abacus.

Most of the schools in the Middle Ages, as you know, were attached to or governed by the monasteries, and the course of study was rather peculiar. After becoming acquainted with Latin, rhetoric (the art of good speaking and writing), and logic (the art of reasoning—or argument), the student often went on to arithmetic, geometry, music and astronomy, but the standards required were very low. The mathematical work mostly involved the ability to keep accounts correctly and to prepare almanacs and calendars, showing the various feast days of the church; and few pupils in geometry went beyond the first five propositions of Euclid.

There were, of course, handicaps to learning which we do not experience today. Men called alchemists had only two aims in life. One was to find an 'elixir of life' which would prolong human life indefinitely, and the other was to be able to change common metals into gold, and as a result of their experiments many

CMXX DIVIDED BY VIII

Operation One: CMXX divided by II.

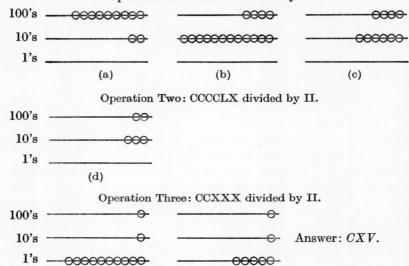

(a)   (b)   (c)

Operation Two: CCCCLX divided by II.

(d)

Operation Three: CCXXX divided by II.

Answer: *CXV*.

(e)   (*f*)

A medieval computer may have worked out the above problem as shown here. First of all, it was necessary to recognize that 8 is equivalent to $2 \times 2 \times 2$. Then the counters would be set out on the abacus as at (a). The hundreds would be divided as at (b), the odd hundred being broken up into 10 tens, the counters being added to the appropriate line as shown. The tens line was then divided by 2 as at (c). Operation Two at (d) was easily accomplished. In operation Three the Hundreds were divided by 2, then the Tens, while the odd Ten was broken up into units as shown at (e). Dividing the units was all that was necessary to be able to read off the answer as at (f).

The development of the abacus is described on pages 156-60.

useful discoveries were made. But knowledge was surrounded by all kinds of fantastic beliefs and superstitions, and further hampered by the scarcity of writing materials and of books, the latter, especially, being so highly expensive that if you had three or four you were considered a very wealthy man. It is not surprising, then, that so little progress was made in those times.

Arithmetic is really the science of numbers, and we know very little about its beginnings. As a science it made but little advance, compared with modern standards, among the ancient Egyptians and the Greeks because of their clumsy number systems. The Greeks, you may remember, turned away from pure arithmetic, while the Romans too, with their number system, were tied to the bead frame for most of their calculations. It was only when the monks and merchants and other mathematicians were set free by an entirely new system, that any substantial progress could be made.

We have read how Fibonacci introduced the new system into Italy, but this was not the only way by which the idea came to Europe. By referring again to the map of Arabic conquests you will see that the Arabs had universities in Spain, particularly at Toledo and Cordova.

In 1085 Toledo was captured from the Arabs—they are more correctly called Moors—and soon European students were flocking into the city to gain all they could from Arabic learning. Among them, about 1120, was an Englishman known as Adelard of Bath. After studying at Toledo, he went on to many other Mediterranean lands, translating the works of the Arabs. Among other things, he was one of the first to translate the works of Euclid into Latin, and the astronomical tables of Alkarismi. Another English scholar was Robert of Chester, who also went to Spain translating into Latin.

You will see that this was a second source by which Arabic numerals entered Europe, and there is one further source which should be mentioned. At Salerno, on the west coast of Italy, a medical university was founded, one of the earliest in Europe, and at one time, the most famous. Here Jewish doctors studied and lectured, translating Arab works into Latin, which in time seeped through to the rest of Europe.

This new arithmetic based on Arabic numerals was given the name, after the work of Alkarismi, of 'algorism' or 'algorithm'. The numerals themselves had undergone some changes, as you can see from the following:

	1	2	3	4	5	6	7	8	9
Gobar									
Early European									

These European numerals are the oldest yet known in any European manuscript and were written in Spain about 976.

One of the earliest works in the English language on this system can still be seen in the British Museum, in London. It is called *The Crafte of Nombryng* and was written about 1300. Here is the introduction to the work, for your interest only:

Here tells that ther ben 7 spices or partes of this craft. The first is called addicion, the secunde is called subtraccion. The thryd is called duplacion. The 4. is called dimyddicion. The 5. is called multiplicacion. The 6. is called diuision. The 7. is called extraccion of the Rote.

The manuscript goes on to say:

Furthermore ye most undrstonde that in this craft ben usid teen figurys, as her writen for ensampul. 9 . 8 . 7 . 6 1

and it goes on to describe the processes of arithmetic.

This arithmetic, and the numerals which are the basis of it, gradually spread throughout Europe, due as much to the makers of calendars and almanacs, and to merchants, as to the men of learning, so that by 1400 they were fairly well known generally.

You have read of the flourishing trade of the Italian cities, and the amount of arithmetic in the form of business transactions and accounts which this necessitated, and the work of the merchants and their clerks, quite obviously, had considerable bearing on the growth of the new arithmetic.

These men, especially the traders of Florence, improved on commercial arithmetic in particular. It was they who began the system of book-keeping by double entry, every transaction being entered on the credit side in one ledger and on the debit side in another. They also arranged the problems of arithmetic into different classes, such as Rule of Three (already mentioned), Interest, Compound Interest, Profit and Loss, Factorage (now known as Brokerage—or Commission), and so on. In addition to this, they reduced the various operations of arithmetic to seven, which they called numeration, addition, subtraction, multiplication, division, raising to powers and extraction of roots.

After these important contributions, which evolved only gradually, there were four other great improvements in the development of arithmetic. These were:

(i) Simplification of the four main processes of arithmetic.

(ii) The development of notation, such as the signs for plus, minus, equality, and for the raising to powers.

(iii) The use of decimal fractions.

(iv) The invention of logarithms.

As regards (i), though arithmetical operations can be very complicated, they are finally reducible to what is known as the four fundamental operations of addition, subtraction, multiplication and division, the last two being somewhat complicated forms of the first two, and subtraction being a reversed form of addition.

There were several systems of multiplication used in Italy in the 15th century, one man called Pacioli publishing a work in 1494 which set down eight plans of multiplication, some of them obtained from Bhaskara's *Lilavati*, but the present system seems to have come about in Florence. This same man, whose work summed up the general mathematical knowledge of his time, also worked out methods of division, and we find that our present method of long division was becoming known by the end of the 15th century.

The other improvements are best discussed separately, in conjunction with the men associated with either their discovery or their improvement.

G

A. Robert Recorde: Plus and Minus Signs and Equality

In glancing through this part of the chapter you may think that this section and those that follow deal more with algebraic symbols than arithmetical ones. This is mostly true, for the symbols of arithmetic are almost entirely those of algebra also, most of them being used with pure number only within the last 150 years or so, partly to help in printing. Though we use them freely today in our arithmetic, the symbols we shall discuss were used, even by those who introduced them, chiefly in connection with algebra, the exceptions being the signs of plus and minus. As Robert Recorde is usually associated with these, we will discuss him first.

Robert Recorde was the most outstanding English mathematician of the 16th century. He went to Oxford about 1525, and later to Cambridge where, in 1545, he received a degree as a doctor. Before this he had taught mathematics in both of these places, though usually in private lessons, but after obtaining his degree he went to London to become a physician to the king, Edward VI, and also to Queen Mary who followed him. Unfortunately, he later got into trouble with the law, possibly for fraud, and he was still in prison when he died.

Recorde is often looked upon as being the founder of the English school of mathematics, for he wrote his works in English, and was quite original in the way he went about it.

He published four books on mathematics and one on medicine, all of them still being in existence, and he probably wrote others which are now lost. The four books on mathematics are written as in conversation, and of these the *Grounde of Artes* was the best known, and was the most successful arithmetic book printed in the 16th century. It gives methods of calculation with both counters and figures, and it includes a good deal of commercial arithmetic, most of it copied from Italy.

It was not, however, the first English book on the subject, for

Recorde says in the *Grounde of Artes* that he hopes some people will like it more than any other English 'Arithmetike' written before, and for 'such as shal lacke instructers . . . I haue plain-ly set forth the examples as no book hath hitherto.'

In the *Grounde of Artes* Recorde indicates the equality of two ratios by parallel lines whose opposite ends are joined, like this: Z . He also uses $+$ for excess and $-$ for deficiency, saying: 'thys figure $+$, whiche betokeneth to muche, as this lyne, $-$ plaine without a cross lyne, betokeneth to lyttle.' But he was not the first man to use these signs, for they first appeared in print in Germany in 1489. No doubt Recorde's work helped to make them better known, though it was some long time before even these were used freely in arithmetic.

Although the *Grounde of Artes* was the most successful account of arithmetic of its day, another book was written on commercial arithmetic some twenty years later, which improved on the work of Recorde and likewise became very popular.

The second of Recorde's works was on astronomy, and in this appeared for the first time in England the new theory evolved by Copernicus, which stated that the sun and not the earth is the centre of our planetary system.

The third book of Recorde was on geometry, being an attempt to summarize the works of Euclid, but his fourth book should be especially remembered. It is called *The Whetstone of Witte*, and in it he introduces our modern sign of $=$. He says: 'I will sette as I doe often in woorke vse, a pair of paralleles, or . . . lines of one lengthe, thus: $=$, bicause noe .2. thynges can be moare equalle'.

Though at one time it was thought that Recorde had improved on an earlier sign, it is now believed that he was the actual inventor of our present symbol for equality. But the symbol itself did not become popular for at least a hundred years, the symbol $\propto$ or ∞ being used instead.

B. *Francois Vieta: Algebraic Notation*

Francois Vieta was the greatest of French mathematicians in

the 16th century. He studied the law and after practising in this for some time, entered parliament. Later he entered the king's service as one of his advisers, and finding himself with more free time, he devoted much of this to the study of mathematics.

Vieta wrote several works, mostly on algebra and geometry. His book *In Artem* is one of the earliest books on symbolic algebra (that is, algebra in which symbols are used), and in it he introduces the use of letters for known and unknown positive numbers.

He is best remembered for two outstanding improvements in the writing of algebra:

(i) He showed known quantities by using consonants such as B, C, D, F, and unknown quantities by using the vowels such as A, E, I, U. In this way he was able to use more than one unknown quantity, though, in this respect, the German Stifel already used a method which was an improvement on this.

(ii) When he used A for our unknown x, he would use A quadratus for A^2, A cubus for A^3, A quadratus quadratus for A^4 (or sometimes Aqq), and so on, which clearly showed the connection between the unknowns.

These improvements were not the only contribution to algebra made by Vieta. Among other things, he tried to prove that a function of the nth degree (for example, containing x^4) is the product of n (in this case, 4) factors of the first degree; he showed how to increase or decrease the roots of an equation; he worked out a method of calculating π by infinite methods (that is, using products which increase without limit); and he applied algebra to geometry in such a way as to start others thinking of the graphical solution of equations (the working-out of equations by means of graphs). He also wrote freely on cubic and quadratic equations, and was said to be an expert at deciphering letters that had been written in code.

The signs used for multiplication and division will be dealt with more fully in the last book. We will just mention that the symbol for multiplication used today is due to a man called

Oughtred who used it in 1631, but it had long been in use in cross multiplication. Often a dot was used to avoid confusion with x, as in $3.2=6$.

Our symbol for division $\div$ was used by Italian merchants in the 15th century to indicate a half as $4\div$, $4\div$, etc. Division was usually denoted by a line between the two figures as $6|3$ or $\frac{6}{3}$. Oughtred employed a colon (:) for a ratio, and the present symbol for division is a combination of these two signs.

C. Michael Stifel: Symbols and Series

This man, a German, was interested in mathematics from childhood. He was a Roman Catholic until he heard the reformer Martin Luther speak, then he became a Protestant. He was so full of enthusiasm that he worked out the date for the end of the world, but when this did not come about as predicted, he found himself in prison and had to rely on Martin Luther to get him out.

He was so obsessed with numbers, that by an amusing line of reasoning he declared that the Pope of Rome, at that time Leo X, was the beast referred to in the Book of Revelations in the Bible.

Stifel's chief work was called *Arithmetica Integra*, the first two books of which are on surds (quantities which cannot be exactly expressed in figures) and incommensurables (mentioned previously). The third book is on algebra. It emphasizes the German idea of using $+$ and $-$, signs which probably originated in the warehouses of Europe, where they were written on sacks to indicate 'surplus' or 'minus' in weight. Stifel, however, uses these signs as symbols of operation as well as abbreviation, which means that he used them just as we do today, and in this respect he was the first European to do so.

He was most interested in series, and he put arithmetical and geometrical series alongside each other and noted four laws concerning them, namely that addition in arithmetic progression corresponds to multiplication in geometric progression, that subtraction corresponds to division, multiplication to the finding of

powers, and division to the extraction of roots. You may understand this a little more clearly when we discuss the discovery
of logarithms.

Stifel also realized that if there were four columns of ten
counters on a bead frame, the second column stood for 10^2, the
third for 10^3, the fourth for 10^4, and so on. He saw, too, that
you could work the opposite way, so that the first column in
the opposite direction stood for 10^{-1}, the next 10^{-2}, etc. He
realized the great importance of these negative exponents, as
the -1 and -2 are called, when he said: 'I might write a whole
book containing the marvellous things relating to numbers, but
I must refrain and leave these things with eyes closed.'

At least, before he turned his back on numbers, he set down
clearly the laws of logarithms, such as:

$$2^2 \times 2^3 = 2^5 \qquad\qquad (2^2)^3 = 2^6$$
$$2^5 \div 2^2 = 2^3 \qquad\qquad (2^6)^{\frac{1}{2}} = 2^3$$

In 1553 Stifel published an edition of a work by another
German writer called the *Coss*, and in this he introduced a further
improvement in algebraic notation. Before this time, R was often
used for the radix x, Z or C for zensus or census (x^2), and C or K
for cubus (x^3). Thus $x^2 + 2x - 8$ would be written: $Zp\ 2Rm\ 8$,
where p and m stood for plus and minus. Stifel's improvement
was that he wrote $1A$, $1AA$, $1AAA$, for the unknown quantity,
its square and its cube, which showed at once and quite clearly
the relationship between them.

Stifel's work brought great advances to the progress of arithmetic and algebra, and he was the most outstanding German
mathematician of his day.

PART THREE—DECIMAL FRACTIONS: CHRISTOFF
RUDOLFF AND SIMON STEVIN

It is not easy to say who was the actual inventor of decimal
fractions, for several writers felt the need for, and had the basic

idea of, such an invention in the 14th and 15th centuries. In particular, an Arab clearly recognized the principle of decimal fractions in the early part of the 15th century, when writing of the value of π. He set it down as:

sah-sah
3   1415926 . . . .

etc., correct to 16 places; a remarkable achievement in itself. As you might expect, 'sah-sah' really stood for complete, or whole, numbers.

One of the first men to show that he fully understood the idea of decimal fractions was Christoff Rudolff, a German about whose life little is known, in a work published in 1530. He showed not only an understanding of the matter, but proved that he could work with them, for he calculated the compound interest on a certain sum of money, using a bar just as we should use a decimal point, like this:

413|4347

We might almost call him the inventor, but his work was not properly understood at the time, and it was left to a Flemish mathematician, Simon Stevin, to publish a thorough account of the use of decimal fractions. Stevin stated the rules for working with these fractions so clearly, that there was little left to add to them, the only improvement necessary being in the setting down, or symbolism, of the fractions.

In a French translation of his work, Stevin adds together these numbers:

27(0)8(1)4(2)7(3), 37(0)6(1)7(2)5(3), 875(0)7(1)8(2)2(3),

and in his explanation he sets them down in this way:

(0)	(1)	(2)	(3)
27	8	4	7
37	6	7	5
875	7	8	2
941	3	0	4

Though the numbers may have looked clumsy to you at first, by his setting them down in this way, you can see how much like our present method Stevin's really was.

Another German called Pitiscus, when writing in 1612 of the sin 10″, uses: 4.85, one of the earliest instances of a dot being used for the separatrix. The idea was not readily adopted, for four years later another writer wrote:

$$314, 1' \, 5' \, ' \, 9' \, ' \, ' \, 2' \, ' \, ' \, ' \, 6' \, ' \, ' \, ' \, ' \, 5' \, ' \, ' \, ' \, ' \, ' \text{ for } 314 \cdot 159265$$

John Napier, about whom we shall read next, used the decimal point system in 1619 in a book in which about two hundred decimal points are used. He saw that a point was enough to separate the whole numbers from the fraction, and wrote down a decimal fraction without an integer (whole number) in front of it.

His colleague, however, also discussed in the next section, wrote 25 375, underlining the decimal fraction, while others used 25|375. Even now the method is not universal, for while we in England write 3·25, in America they write 3.25, and in Germany and France 3,25.

You may think that a long period elapsed between the use of the bead frame with its columns of ten, and the introduction of decimal fractions, which is really only a backward continuation of the decimal place value method. This is quite true, and the reason is that, while ordinary fractions are something quite real to us in our everyday lives, the use of decimal fractions is confined mostly to more involved problems, making their solution easier. It was when involved problems gradually became more numerous that decimal fractions appeared.

The invention of logarithms, our fourth development, brought decimal fractions into much greater use, as did the introduction of the French metric system. The use of decimal fractions meant an important advance in the history of mathematics, for without them our modern methods of calculation would be severely restricted.

PART FOUR—THE INVENTION OF LOGARITHMS: JOHN
NAPIER AND HENRY BRIGGS

'Logarith' really means 'ratio number', and the word was
introduced by the man who laid the foundation of modern
logarithms, John Napier, who was born in Edinburgh in 1550
and died in 1617. Napier was an engineer and a physicist, as
well as a mathematician, and he is said to have devised plans
for powerful artillery, 'burning mirrors of great power', a 'chariot'
which was capable of great destruction, and 'devises of sayling
under water'.

But he is best known for his work on logarithms, and though
you are already familiar with these and the laws underlying them,
we will try to explain how Napier got his idea.

His first approach was by means of geometric progressions,
those numbers which increase or decrease as they are multiplied
or divided by a common ratio. We will choose the simplest of
all for our purposes: 1, 2, 4, 8 . . . . Now if we set this progression down under the arithmetic progression of 1, 2, 3, 4, ...
we have:

Arithmetic
Progression 0 1 2 3 4 5 6 7 8 9 10
Geometric
Progression 1 2 4 8 16 32 64 128 256 512 1,024

Quite obviously, the product of any two terms in the lower
line is itself a term further along the row, for example, 8×32
comes to 256, all of which terms are part of the geometric progression. Notice particularly that 256 stands under the figure 8
in the arithmetic progression, while 8 and 32 in the lower row
are under 3 and 5 respectively. You will now see that if we look
for the arithmetic numbers of 8 and 32 (namely 3 and 5), add
these together and go along the arithmetic row till we get to
this new number (8), by referring to the number underneath it
in the geometric row, we are given the answer to the product

of our two original numbers. If you do not follow this, read carefully through this paragraph again until you do, then try it out with other products.

This is what Stifel meant when he said that addition in arithmetic progression corresponds to multiplication in geometric progression, and that subtraction corresponds to division. To put the whole matter into language which you should understand, we say that the log. of 8 to the base of 2 is *3*, while the log. of 32 to the same base is *5*. Therefore the answer to 8 × 32 is the antilog. of *3 plus 5* in our table.

John Napier did not use such simple series as we have, of course, but this, very roughly, was how he got his idea of shortening methods of calculation, and he began working out a series of tables based on this system to help him in the multiplication of sines in trigonometry. He did not start as we did, with small numbers, but began with 10,000,000 and he worked backwards by multiplying, not as we did by 2, but by the fraction:

$$\frac{9,999,999}{10,000,000}$$

so obtaining two sets of numbers, one an arithmetical and the other a geometrical progression.

Napier worked away for twenty years on this idea, and when he had completed his tables he had no real knowledge of the existence of a base, such as 2 in our example. He introduced the word logarithm to replace the term 'artificial number' which he had used for his upper row, and he said that it showed the 'number of the ratios', or the number of times his chosen figure, 10,000,000, had been multiplied by his ratio. The tables were first published in Edinburgh in 1614, in a book called *Descriptio*, and from it eventually arose our modern logarithms.

Soon better ideas of applying the principle were worked out partly by Napier himself, but more particularly by a man called Briggs, who, on reading the *Descriptio*, wrote:

Napier, lord of Markinston, hath set my head and hands at work with his new and admirable logarithms. I hope to see him this summer, if it please God; for I never saw a book which pleased me better, and made me more wonder.

Henry Briggs had been born some fifty-three years earlier, in 1561, and had been educated at Cambridge. He had become a professor of geometry at that university in 1596, and later became the first professor of geometry at both London and Oxford Universities.

He visited Napier in 1615, and the two became great friends. He suggested that it might be more useful if the base of Napier's logarithms was changed to 10, and Napier, who had already begun to think along similar lines, agreed.

So, after long and detailed work, and in co-operation with Napier, Briggs published in 1624 tables of logarithms worked out to 14 decimal places, of numbers from 1 to 20,000 and from 90,000 to 100,000.

He began by making a table of antilogarithms, using the equations:

(i) $$10^{\frac{p}{q}} = \sqrt[q]{10^p}$$

(ii) $$\log_{10} \sqrt[q]{10^p} = \frac{p}{q}$$

(iii) $$\text{antilog}_{10} \frac{p}{q} = \sqrt[q]{10^p}$$

and to get a table of logarithms Briggs applied the rules set down by Stifel. Of course, he used much more complicated numbers in the lower row, namely fractional ones, and he calculated their corresponding numbers to the base of 10 in the upper row. It was a laborious process, and great credit is due to him for his persistence, though a little later, a Dutchman living in London, Adrian Vlacq, published complete logarithmic tables by filling in the gap from 20,000 to 90,000.

Were it not for the painstaking work of Briggs, it is quite possible that Napier's work would have escaped notice for a long time, and the progress of mathematics would have been held back for many years, for by his enthusiasm he convinced not only his colleagues in this country, but the outstanding mathematicians of Germany, Italy and France of the advantages of using logarithms.

Though this was his chief contribution to the history of mathematics, Briggs wrote several other works on geometry, trigonometry and navigation, and is often credited with bringing into everyday use our present method of long division.

To conclude this section on logarithms, we might say that the difference between the logarithms of Napier and the ones we use today, is that while Napier began at 10,000,000 and called its logarithm 0, we begin at 1 and call its logarithm 0. Also, instead of multiplying by Napier's minute fraction, we generally use the base of 10.

In all fairness, we should mention one other name in connection with logarithms, that of Jobst Burgi, a Swiss. He evidently discovered them independently about 1610, but by the time his tables were published, Napier's logarithms were being generally admired throughout Europe, so that they did not have quite the same impact on mathematical thought.

Napier's work on logarithms is all the more noteworthy because it is the first really valuable contribution to the history of mathematics by any British writer. As a prominent man, Lord Moulton, said some years ago: 'The invention of logarithms came on the world as a bolt from the blue.'

Its discovery was indeed unique, for it was unrelated to any previous work, nor had earlier mathematicians even suggested its invention.

We might summarize this whole chapter by saying that the history of elementary arithmetic was influenced by the following five factors:

1. The introduction of the decimal place system of Hindu-Arabic numerals.
2. The simplification of methods of calculation.
3. The development of notation, and the introduction of signs.
4. The introduction of decimal fractions.
5. The invention of logarithms.

TYPICAL EXAMINATION QUESTIONS
BASED ON THIS CHAPTER

1. Write a short account of:
    (a) Logarithms.
    (b) The history of the commoner symbols of mathematics.

2. Write short accounts of:
    (a) The sign for equality (=) we now use.
    (b) The introduction of logarithms.

3. Give an account of the origin of the symbols which are now used for equality and for the four elementary processes of arithmetic.

4. Trace the development of the symbols for the common operations in arithmetic and algebra.

5. Describe the contributions made to mathematics by:
    (a) Vieta.
    (b) Briggs.

6. Write an essay on either of the following:
    (a) The life and work of Robert Recorde.
    (b) The invention of logarithms.

7. The invention of decimal fractions was one of the most important single improvements in the art of calculation. Give an account of the history of this invention and explain its importance.

8. Give an account of the early history of logarithms.

Book Three

THE SEVENTEENTH CENTURY AND AFTER

1: THE EXPANSION OF MATHEMATICS

W E now come to the stage where it is extremely difficult to deal with the history of mathematics as a single continuous story. You may have noticed already how the subject is expanding, and this development continued even more rapidly in the 17th century, as mathematics asserted itself in so many other sciences and became an important factor in their development also.

In continuing our account we have two choices before us. Either we can try to trace in turn the various branches of mathematics, dealing with new discoveries and those responsible for them as they arise, or we can deal with the lives of each of the most important of these people, introducing their contributions to mathematics in general, no matter in what field. The latter method, popular in books of this kind, is the method we shall now adopt. However, later on in Book Four we will discuss certain topics separately to give some idea of their general development.

Though it is not quite true to say that this century or that was the most important in the development of mathematics in general, it is true to say that the 17th century saw a more rapid development than any other before it.

Apart from the expansion of trade and the calculations and book-keeping of the merchant classes which this necessitated, there were other reasons for this. First, the improvement in printing (invented at the end of the 15th century) was of considerable help. As books gradually became cheaper, the reading public widened, which, in turn, encouraged people to ponder and think for themselves. The inventor could make his discoveries known more quickly. Furthermore, printing tended, especially later on, to bring about a little more uniformity of expression, both in spelling and in mathematics.

Religion, too, which persistently clung to the ideas of the old philosophers, was losing some of its stranglehold on men's minds. Though, as we shall shortly see, organized religion was reluctant to relax this grip, as the years of this century rolled on, it found itself obliged to be less intolerant in the face of learning if it still wished to hold its place in the lives of the people.

Next came the inventions and improvements of the time. In military affairs mathematics was playing its part. Old prints are still in existence which show how mathematicians calculated the angle of elevation of a cannon in order to be able to bombard an objective with cannon balls.

Mathematics was also necessary in the building of ships, particularly as they were being constructed on a bigger scale and in a more seaworthy fashion. It was finding an important place in navigation, where various instruments were devised for plotting a ship's course and finding its true position at sea.

The surveying and levelling of land and the construction of canals required particular skill, and made those who undertook these things study mathematics of one kind or another.

Books on machines were written even before the invention of printing, and also on architecture, for though we are often inclined to think of the Industrial Revolution as beginning about 1700, machines were in operation long before this time, particularly in Italy in the later Middle Ages, where in Lucca and Venice a silk industry was established in the 14th century based on water power.

In the 15th century mining also developed in Europe, using pumps and hoisting machinery which, though often crude, showed some understanding of mathematics.

You will have heard also of Leonardo da Vinci, the Italian genius, himself a mathematician of outstanding ability, whose work in this direction was overshadowed by his other contributions to science and art. You may have read how he could build assault engines, tunnels—even beneath rivers—aqueducts, and of how he drew up plans for a submarine and an aeroplane so effectively that modern engineers have been astonished at his ability and foresight, all of which required a deep understanding of geometry and applied mathematics.

The making and perfection of clocks, useful in astronomy and navigation as well as in everyday life, required great skill and interested those who handled them in machinery and mechanics in general.

Furthermore, when the telescope was invented man's horizon was greatly enlarged. Though the earliest telescopes were crude compared with their modern counterparts, they were satisfactory enough, as we shall see, to enable men to calculate the paths of heavenly bodies, and this, again, required some knowledge of mathematics, especially of geometry.

Lastly, there was a new spirit abroad amongst men of science. To these men it did not matter quite so much now which country you belonged to, but rather if you had something to contribute to the ever-widening field of learning. As a result ideas were more freely exchanged. Scholars were invited from one country to another, either by a private individual, such as a prince or a king, or by seats of learning, such as the universities, or by societies.

In view of all this, you may now realize how difficult our task is becoming. Within the limits of this book we can deal only with the most important developments in mathematics, and the most outstanding men who made them.

2: GALILEO. 1564-1642

GALILEO GALILEI, to give him his full name, was born at Pisa in Italy. His early schooling was carried out in a monastery, but later he was taken away by his father and sent to the university of Pisa to study medicine.

One day when he was 19 years old, Galileo's attention was attracted to the swinging motion of a lamp in the draughty cathedral of Pisa. Galileo timed its movements (known as oscillations) by means of his pulse, and it seemed to him that these were carried out in equal times, no matter whether the swing of the lamp be long or short. When he got home he experimented with various shapes of wood and metal suspended on short and long strings, and by this means he eventually established what is known as the isochronism of the pendulum (that is, the constant time of a pendulum of given length); a fact of which the Arabs had been aware, but of which no one apparently had taken much notice. This principle was soon applied to medical diagnosis, and it brought about an important advance in that sphere. It was also used later, and is still in use, in the construction of clocks.

Up to this time Galileo had been rather ignorant of mathematics, but hearing by chance a lecture on geometry, he was so fascinated that he decided to discard his medical studies and devote most of his time instead to this new interest.

Partly through a lack of money and partly through his habit of arguing with his teachers on the things they expected him to believe, he had to abandon his studies at the university, but he soon became known through his essays and demonstrations. In particular, his studies of the works of Archimedes led him to the invention of the hydrostatic balance (an instrument used for finding the specific gravity of substances in water), and an essay on this made him famous, while another work on centres of gravity obtained for him a mathematical appointment at Pisa university.

Another of his theories was that two objects released together will fall to the ground in the same time. Previously it was believed that a two-pound weight would fall twice as fast as a one-pound weight, and so on. So the other university professors laughed at him; but Galileo was determined to belittle them instead. Climbing to the top of the famous leaning tower of Pisa, before a large number of students and professors he released, among other things, a half-pound weight and a hundred-pound cannon ball at exactly the same moment. They struck the ground almost at the same instant, and would have done so exactly but for the resistance of the air. Unfortunately, Galileo's manner over these demonstrations gave such offence to his colleagues that he was obliged to resign from his post at the university, though in the following year, 1592, he found an even better one at Padua.

Here he concentrated mostly on mechanics (the motion and equilibrium—or balance—of forces) and hydrostatics (the science of liquids at rest). He experimented on inclines and found that the ratio of increase in speed of bodies on these was constant. For vertical fall he discovered that the speed increased at a rate of 32 feet per second every second. Thus, after ten seconds it would be 320 feet per second, while the distance covered could be found by the formula:

$$\frac{\text{Number of Seconds} \times \text{Maximum Speed of Fall}}{2}$$

Among other things, Galileo proved that the path of a projectile (any body propelled forward by force, such as a stone thrown into the air, or a cannon ball shot from a gun) is a parabola; he probably invented a thermometer, and made some useful discoveries on the magnet. He taught his students to measure the heights of mountains by their shadows, and tried to measure the speed of light by means of observers flashing lights from opposite mountains, one light being flashed on as soon as the other was seen, but he found the interval too short to be measured.

In addition to all of this, Galileo was a keen astronomer. He had previously heard of an optician who had made a tube containing lenses, and this set him working on the construction of a telescope. He produced one of three-fold magnifying power, and had soon improved on this with one magnifying by thirty diameters, so that he was able to publish observations on the sun, the moon and the planets. As a result of this, his instruments were in demand by other scientists, including his proportional or sector compasses which he invented and which were useful to engineers and architects. Many of these instruments Galileo made with his own hands.

His observations of the heavens convinced him that an earlier astronomer we have already mentioned, Copernicus, was correct when he stated that the sun was the centre of our planetary system, but he was afraid to announce this owing to the religious beliefs and prejudices of the time. But a further discovery, that of the little moons of Jupiter, convinced him of the correctness of the Copernican theory, as it is called, and he set to work on a book written in dialogue in which three friends meet and discuss rival theories.

In 1632 he published these dialogues on the system of the world. He was called to Rome, forced to say he was sorry for what he had written, obliged to do a penance, and set free only on condition that he would be 'obedient' in the future. He took up his work on mechanics again, and wrote a book on the subject in 1636. Though the next year he became blind, he continued his experiments in mechanics and on the pendulum.

One of Galileo's most important discoveries in mechanics is that once a body is set in motion it will tend to go on moving in a straight line at a steady speed for ever. Only when force is exerted on the body will it slow down or turn aside. You may doubt this, as a rolling ball or a bicycle does stop, but there are several forces acting on these moving bodies. This theory of Galileo's played an important part in the future of astronomy, for once it was accepted there was no longer any mystery as to why a planet continued its movement once it was set in motion. The only problem left was, why should they move in curves round the sun, instead of in a straight line? The answer was supplied some years later by Sir Isaac Newton.

We can summarize Galileo's work in this way. By his endeavours he established mechanics as a science. His work on dynamics (the action of force) showed that he realized that motion and force depended on each other, and in this way he prepared the ground for Sir Isaac Newton's discoveries later. He made such amazing advances because he experimented freely and calculated from the results of his experiments, thus working out in theory what he had discovered in practice. He stated clearly that science must be founded on experiment, and adopted this method in his investigations of falling bodies, of equilibrium, of motion on inclined planes and of a projectile. He made excellent observations and deductions in astronomy, though he did not make any tremendous advance in the science itself. He is sometimes looked upon as one of the mathematicians linking the 16th century with the mathematics of our own times.

3: KEPLER. 1571-1630

JOHANN KEPLER is perhaps best remembered as one of the founders of modern astronomy rather than as a mathematician, but we include him here because he was also a geometer and algebraist of considerable ability.

He was born in Germany of humble parents; his father kept a public house, and his mother was later brought to trial as a witch. Though he had to help considerably in the home, he won a scholarship to a university and started training as a clergyman, but when he graduated he became a teacher instead, and then devoted most of his time to the study of astronomy.

He believed that the world was created according to a very simple pattern and he set out to discover it. He thought that it was connected with the periods of revolution of the several planets and the sizes of their orbits, and in 1596 he wrote a book setting this idea out. About the only good thing this book did was to bring his name to the notice of a Danish astronomer called Tycho Brahe, who was about to settle in Prague and was looking for a new assistant. This Tycho Brahe had collected an enormous amount of observations on the planets, and when Kepler was taken on by his master, he tried to apply these observations to his idea of the solar system.

After Tycho Brahe died Kepler worked away for years, calculating and re-calculating, trying to fit the figures into his scheme by employing all kinds of methods, sometimes with a near accuracy. He thought that the sun gave out rays of force somewhat like the spokes of a gigantic wheel, and as the sun turned round these rays of force pushed the planets along. For some strange reason, Kepler also thought it would follow that the farther away a planet would be the slower it would move.

When Kepler tried out this theory on the observations of the planet Mars, he found that its orbit could not possibly be a circle. This was where he had gone wrong, for until this time he had believed that all planets travelled in true circles round the sun. He had sufficient confidence in the figures left by his master not to discard them, and when he fitted them to an ellipse he found that they worked out, not only for Mars, but for the other planets including the Earth.

This enabled him to set down his first two laws of planetary motion, which were published in 1609, and to these he added a third in 1619. Here are Kepler's laws, and they are worth remembering, for it was these laws which gave Isaac Newton the clue to the law of universal gravitation.

1. Every planet travels round the sun in an ellipse, the sun occurring as one focus (this being one of two points having a definite relationship in the ellipse).
2. The speed of a planet increases as it gets nearer to the sun, and decreases as it gets farther away, but the radius vector (an imaginary line joining the centre of the planets to the centre of the sun) sweeps over equal areas in equal times.
3. The time a planet takes to go round the sun depends on its distance from the sun, and the square of the time it takes will be in proportion to the cube of its average distance away.

You may be able to follow these laws a little more clearly by referring to the diagram on the next page. Though it is a simple matter to state them now, it was a wonderful achievement to have found them out so long ago.

Working on Tycho Brahe's figures in conjunction with these laws, Kepler produced a set of planetary tables which were superior to any previous ones. They also led him to the suspicion that it was the sun which caused the planets to move in orbits of this shape.

Such a great contribution to astronomy tends to overshadow Kepler's mathematical achievements. In 1613 his attention was drawn to the defective way in which the cubical contents of vessels used in wine-making were calculated. He became interested in the volumes of solids and wrote an essay on the subject, in which he worked out volumes by rotating parts of conic sections about an axis. His circle, for instance, was made up of minute triangles, all with their apex at the centre of the circle, and his sphere was made up of tiny pointed pyramids. This method of

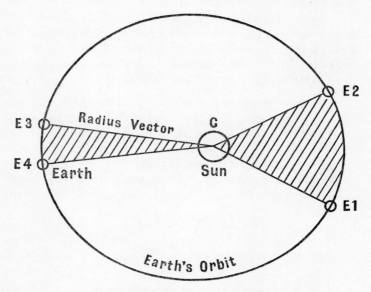

DIAGRAM ILLUSTRATING KEPLER'S LAWS

(*Note:* The diagram is not in proportion.)

1. Every planet describes an ellipse round the Sun, the Sun occurring as one focus.
2. The radius vector sweeps over equal areas in equal times. (This means that if the Earth travels from E1 to E2 in the same time as it travels from E3 to E4, the area of the shaded portion E1 E2 C is the same as the area of the shaded portion E3 E4 C.)
3. The square of the times that two planets take to go round the sun will be in proportion to the cube of their mean distance away. This means that if T be the time a planet takes to go round the Sun and M be its mean distance from the Sun, then a direct proportion exists between T^2 and M^3. This applies to all the planets. Mars, for instance, takes approximately 1·88 years to complete its orbit, and is 1·52 times as far as the Earth from the Sun.

$$1·88^2 = 3·53 \text{ and } 1·52^3 = 3·5 \text{ (to 3 figures).}$$

calculation showed that he had some basic idea of the infinitesimal calculus, a method of calculating by using an infinite number of minute quantities, of which we shall hear more later.

In this connection also, his theories above made it necessary to find the area of focal sectors, that is, a part of an ellipse defined by two radii from the focus and the arc between them (the shaded portions in the diagram). His method is called the 'sum of the radii', and is a kind of integration, a part of the calculus concerned with the adding up of minute parts.

In a series of tables published in 1620, Kepler used logarithms, appreciating their great advantages. He worked hard to encourage their general use, and in 1627 he produced new logarithm tables which could be used in astronomy, and these were popular for over a hundred years.

Apart from being interested in conic sections, Kepler also studied optics, and he wrote a work setting down his ideas on refraction (the deflection of light and heat). In addition, he gave an explanation of the telescope, and described an improved type, based on two convex lenses, which later became quite common.

4: DESCARTES. 1596-1650

I f you like to lie late in bed in the morning, you can claim to have something in common with one of the greatest French mathematicians of the 17th century. The only difference may be that while you enjoy lazing your time away, René Descartes enjoyed thinking.

Descartes got into this habit when a boy, for he was very weak in health, and when he was old enough to attend school he was still allowed to stay in bed as long as he wished. In fact, he did much of his mental work in bed, for though frail in body, he was active in mind; so much so that his father often called him the 'Little Philosopher'.

After leaving school in 1612, Descartes went to Paris, but later enlisted in the Dutch army. One day a mathematical problem was posted in a public place by a mathematician who chalenged anyone to find the correct answer. Descartes solved this problem in a few hours, and this so encouraged him that he lost his enthusiasm for the army and devoted all the spare time he could to mathematical studies. A few years later he gave up his army life and spent five years in travel, during which time he continued to study not only mathematics, but also philosophy, that is, the relationship between God and Nature and Man.

When he returned to Paris, his friends would not leave him alone, often disturbing him in bed while he was writing his notes, so in 1628 he went back to Holland and stayed there, often moving about in secret so as to be able to carry out his work undisturbed.

He prepared a work on philosophy, but after the persecution of Galileo (see p. 108) he decided not to publish it. He then devoted himself to a work on universal science, and to this he added three books which were really appendices or additions to the former work.

One of these appendices was entitled *La Géométrie*, and in it what is now known as analytical geometry appeared in print for the first time. Speaking in a general way, analytical geometry is a merging of algebra with geometry. You may have noticed how arithmetic and algebra have been developing gradually, while geometry so far has made almost no progress at all since the time of the Greeks. Now, in this work of Descartes, algebra and geometry were brought together to form a higher branch of the latter science.

The idea of the analytical geometry of Descartes was to try to make algebra clearer by applying geometrical methods to it —in other words, what we call today the graphic treatment of equations. He was not by any means the first mathematician to apply geometry to algebra—even Archimedes had done so— but the advance made by Descartes was that he saw that the position of any point in a plane (a flat surface) could be found if its distances, called co-ordinates (x and y) are given or calculated from two fixed lines at right angles, called axes; really an extension of the old idea of latitude and longitude.

Descartes realized also that though an indeterminate equation (mentioned on p. 58) can be answered by an infinite number of values for x and y, yet a few of these values determine the position of several points which, when joined up, form a curve, the equation $f(x, y=0)$ expressing a relationship that is true for every point on the curve. Therefore, by means of calculations based on the equation, the results could be transferred to form such a curve.

Descartes went still further. He saw that by using the same system of co-ordinates (often called the scales), two or even more curves can be referred to the same axes, and that where the two or more curves intersect can be found the roots (if you prefer, the unknown quantities) which the equations have in common. This discovery is sometimes said to be 'The greatest single step ever made in the progress of exact sciences'.

If you have already learnt to solve equations by means of graphs you will understand more clearly what all this is about. Also, you will know that the straight line produced by a 'linear equation' is usually referred to as a 'curve' in this particular work.

Descartes' *Géométrie* is divided into three books. In the first he explains the principles of analytical geometry, relating the operations of arithmetic to it. In the second book he classifies curves into 'geometrical' and 'mechanical' curves. Geometrical curves he classifies again into curves of increasing difficulty, such as the circle, parabola, ellipse and so on, the straight line being also included in this group. Mechanical curves are much more complicated ones, and he does not discuss these in great detail.

In the third book Descartes analyses algebra as it was then known, and in this book he made several important contributions to the subject. He was the first mathematician to adopt our present system of using the first letters of the alphabet to represent known quantities, and the last letters, x, y, z, to represent unknowns. He also introduced our present system of indices, though even he often used xx for x^2, and he understood negative quantities and used them in his work.

He gave a rule for solving equations which was substantially this:

'Write the equation in zero form (such as $x^2+x-12=0$); try to factorize the left-hand side, so as to reduce the equation to two or more equations of lower degree. If this is impossible, higher methods are to be used.'

He stated that if the equation is of the third or fourth degree (involving x^3 or x^4) the solution depended on the intersection of a circle with a conic. To solve equations of still higher degree, he proposed using the intersection of a circle with more complicated geometric curves, believing that equations of any degree could be solved in this way; but in this he was wrong.

Descartes is also remembered for his 'Rule of Signs'. This is to the effect that an equation can have no more 'true' (that is, positive) roots than its coefficients have changes of sign from plus to minus, and no more 'false' (that is, negative) roots than the number of times two plus or two minus signs occur in succession. If you would like an example on this, consider the equation:

$$x^4-x^3-x^2+x-1=0$$

As this equation has three changes of sign, it cannot have more than three positive roots. Since two minus signs occur in succession only once, and two plus signs not at all, the equation can have only one negative root.

Descartes also wrote a system of the universe based upon the idea of whirlpools of matter, or vortices, and his works on philosophy have earned him the title of 'the father of modern philosophy'. In this book, however, we should remember him for his work on analytical geometry and algebra.

When Queen Christina of Sweden heard of the fame of Descartes, she asked him to go to Stockholm as her tutor. But the extreme cold, and the fact that the queen wanted her lessons at peculiar times—even in the early hours of the morning— undermined his health, and he died soon after in 1650.

THE CYCLOID

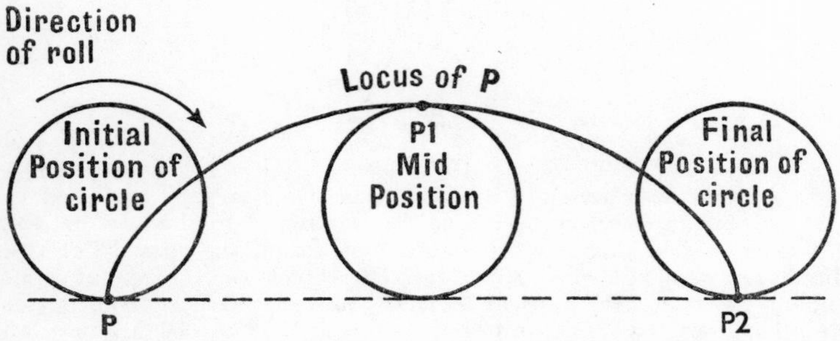

Direction
of roll

Locus of P

Initial
Position of
circle

P1
Mid
Position

Final
Position of
circle

P

P2

This curve is the locus of a point on the circumference of a circle which rolls, without sliding, along a fixed straight line. It is shown for one revolution.

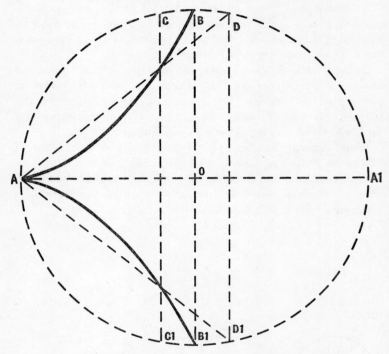

THE CISSOID (IVY-SHAPED CURVE)

This curve was invented by the Greek Diocles, and was used to give a solution to the problem of duplicating the cube (see p. 42).

Diocles had a simple method of constructing the curve. Let two diameters of a circle, AOA_1 and BOB_1 bisect each other at right angles. Draw chords parallel to BOB_1 and equidistant from it (for simplicity only two, CC_1 and DD_1 are shown). Then the intersection of AD and CC_1, and AD_1 and CC_1, etc., will give the points which form the curve.

5: FERMAT. 1601-1665

PIERRE DE FERMAT was a Frenchman who is sometimes called the greatest writer on the theory of numbers. His only education he received at home, but though a very modest man, he later became a member of parliament in Toulouse. He really seems something of a mystery, for he did not study mathematics seriously until he was thirty, and though he must have been aware of his outstanding ability in the subject, his work has become known only through the letters he wrote to other famous men, or through odd sheets of paper or margin notes found after his death.

Soon after he took up his work as a councillor, he started to devote his spare time to mathematics. His achievements were in three directions, namely:

(i) The theory of numbers.

(ii) Geometry.

(iii) Problems on probability.

As regards (i) he wrote numerous theorems, though most of his proofs are lost, and, in any case, they are too involved for our consideration here.

However, one is of special note, and is called 'Fermat's Last Theorem'. It states that no integral value of x, y, and z can be found to satisfy the equation:

$$x^n + y^n = z^n$$

if n stands for an integer greater than 2.

This problem, whose general solution has baffled mathematicians since his time, has been responsible for a great amount of modern geometry, and for numerous theorems on numbers. It has been proved for many values of n, but there is, as yet, no proof for all values of n. Fermat stated that he had one, but if he did it has never been discovered. The theorem itself is not really so important as the enormous amount of mathematics which has been worked out in the attempts to solve it.

It is known that in geometry Fermat had the idea of analytical geometry before Descartes, and that he was the first man to apply it to geometry of three dimensions. He studied curves, such as the ellipse, the cycloid and the cissoid (the 'ivy-shaped' curve—see p. 118) and others, and he drew tangents to these and solved their quadrature (that is, you may remember, finding a square exactly equal to their area).

This work is all the more outstanding because to it he applied the idea of infinitesimals. This is a subject beyond the scope of this book, but we can mention that an infinitesimal is a minute variation—or change in a quantity—whose numerical value becomes so small that it approaches zero, and by dealing mathematically with such minute quantities and their relationship to other quantities, it is possible to work out many otherwise almost insoluble problems.

By the use of infinitesimals Fermat solved several problems on the curves mentioned above, as well as solving problems on the centres of figures and masses. Isaac Newton said that he got the idea of his calculus, which we shall mention later, from some of Fermat's work.

With Pascal, whom we shall discuss next, Fermat founded a theory known as the 'Theory of Probability'. Fermat had been sent a problem roughly as follows:

A game of skill was being played by two players who wished to retire before the game was finished. If the number of points which make up the game are known, and also the scores of the two players, in what proportion should they divide the money at stake according to their chances of winning at that particular stage of the game?

Fermat's solution depended on the theory of combinations. In case you may be sufficiently interested, I will quote from another book* an example given by Fermat in a letter to Pascal. Suppose the two players are A and B, and A wants two points to win and B three points. Then:

'The game will be decided in the course of four trials. Take the letters *a* and *b*, and write down all the combinations that can be formed of four letters. These combinations are 16 in number, namely, *aaaa, aaab, aaba, aabb; abaa, abab, abba, abbb; baaa, baab, baba, babb; bbaa, bbab, bbba, bbbb*. Now every combination in which *a* occurs twice or oftener represents a case favourable to A, and every combination in which *b* occurs three times or oftener represents a case favourable to B. Thus, on counting them, it will be found that there are 11 cases favourable to A, and 5 cases favourable to B; and since these cases are all equally likely, A's chance of winning the game is to B's chance as 11 is to 5.'

Perhaps it should be pointed out here how careful we should be with the use of the terms 'combinations' and 'permutations', the latter really being an extension of the principle of combinations. When we speak of a combination we are only concerned with the number of things in a certain selection, the order being of no importance, but when we speak of permutations we are not only concerned with the number of things in a certain selection, but also the order in which they are placed.

From this you will see that in the extract above the word 'combination' is used very loosely and 'permutation' would be the more appropriate term. Such a loose reference to these two things, however, is very common today, for even in our modern gambling the terms are generally misused. It is not the intention of this chapter to introduce you to gambling methods, but it is very curious that the term permutation in connection with football pools should really be 'combination', and the term combination as used in greyhound racing should really be 'permutation'.

If you are keen enough to pursue this matter, have you seen something like this in a newspaper, or on a football coupon?

* *A Short History of Mathematics*, by W. W. Rouse Ball. Macmillan & Co., page 300.

POOL X

FOUR AWAYS

Addlemere	v	Trundle	2									
Bagsworthy	v	Deepdale	2	A								
Cuddletown	v	Mead	2		Perm 2 of A with 2 of B							
Doddington	v	Greenacre										
Elmsleigh	v	Redthrop	2		9 lines at 6d. = 4s. 6d.							
Foxmore	v	Nethershot		B								
Grindle	v	Tipdown	2									
Hogsmorton	v	Pottle	2									

What is really meant here is 'combine' 2 of A with 2 of B.
If, for simplicity, we refer to each chosen team by its initial
letter, we have nine possible combinations, namely: ABEG,
ABEH, ABGH, ACEG, ACEH, ACGH, BCEG, BCEH, and
BCGH. Notice particularly that the same four letters do not
appear together more than once, though each combination can
be rearranged in four different ways. For instance, if we consider the first combination, ABEG, we can set this down as:
ABEG, BAEG, ABGE, and BAGE. Thus there can be thirty-six
permutations altogether and not nine as stated on the above
'coupon'.

At a greyhound meeting, a gambler might choose three dogs,
which we will call 1, 2, 3, and may wish to back them for a first
and second place. At the Tote he buys a 'combination' forecast
on his choice, which in this case would be six cards bearing the
numbers: 1 2; 2 1; 1 3; 3 1; 2 3; 3 2. As you can see, this is not
a combination at all, but is a permutation of two out of three
dogs chosen.

There is no need for you to remember any of this. It is introduced merely as a topic of interest, and it is hoped that you
have found the diversion refreshing rather than illuminating!

To return to the life of Fermat, it is necessary to add that all
of his work shows him to have been a brilliant mathematician.
Though he and Pascal agreed, for instance, on the final solution

to the problem set above, Fermat's theories on the subject were much more accurate than were those of his colleague. The fact that Fermat wrote so little, and also that he never took the trouble to get his writings published as did men of much less ability, meant a great loss to the science of mathematics.

6 : PASCAL. 1623-1662

N o t every boy has a father who will give up his job and move to another place in order to educate his son. Yet that was one reason that the father of Blaise Pascal moved to Paris. The other reason was that, being a clever mathematician, he wished to go on studying himself.

Blaise, like Descartes, showed outstanding ability at an early age, and under the personal tuition of his father, began the study of ancient languages, all mathematical books being withheld from him so that he should master the languages first. But you know what an attraction forbidden things are to a boy, and soon Pascal discovered geometry for himself, and had already made considerable progress in the subject before he was found out, discovering many of the properties of figures, including that of the sum of the angles in a triangle. So impressed was he by his son's ability in this direction, that Pascal senior relented, and gave Blaise a copy of Euclid's *Elements*, which he soon learnt by heart.

Soon geometry was a mere plaything to him, particularly conic sections—the ellipse, parabola and hyperbola—and when he was 16 he wrote an essay on conics which Descartes refused at first to recognize as the boy's work, believing it to be the work of the father.

One of his essays on the geometry of conics at this time set down what is known as 'Pascal's Theorem'. Briefly, it states that if a hexagon be inscribed in a conic, the points of intersection of the opposite sides will lie in a straight line (see p. 125). From this he worked out over four hundred corollaries (propositions which follow naturally upon one that has already been proved).

At 19 Pascal invented a calculating machine, and when he improved on this a few years later, he became a real pioneer in the making of mechanical aids to calculation. He became

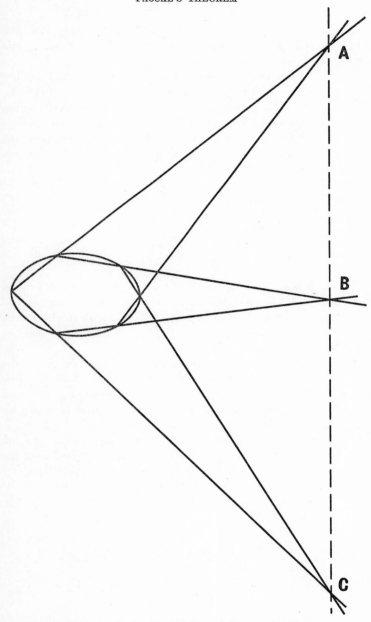

A, B, and C are the points of intersection of the opposite sides of the hexagon inscribed in the ellipse, and these points are collinear (in the same straight line).

known also as a physicist and his works and writings on the equilibrium of fluids, establish him, like Galileo, as one of the founders of the science of hydrodynamics.

For a time Pascal gave up all of these researches to study religion, but when he had to take over his father's affairs, he carried on with his experiments. He wrote at such great lengths of the triangular arrangement of the co-efficients of the powers of a binomial expression (such as $a+b$), that this arrangement is now known as Pascal's Triangle. It is constructed as you see here:

```
I   I   I   I  ╱ I   I
I   2   3  ╱4   5   6
I   3 ╱ 6   10  15  21
I ╱ 4   10  20  35  56
I   5   15  35  70  126
```

You will notice that after the first line each figure is formed by adding together the previous row as far as the number immediately above it. For example, the third figure in the fourth row is 10, because 6 is immediately above it and 3 and 1 are to the left of it.

The top row of figures is called numbers of the first order, the second row of the second order, and so on. If you wish to prove the use of the arrangement, work out the expression $(a+b)^3$ and see what your coefficients come to. They should be as shown by the diagonal line running from right to left, namely, $1+3+3+1$. By drawing further diagonals in this way you can find the co-efficients for higher powers of such expressions. Pascal used his 'triangle' for this, and also in connection with combinations.

Here is another arrangement:

```
                1
            1       1
        1       2       1
      1     3       3       1
    1     4     6     4       1
  1     5     10    10     5       1
```

Can you find the rule for obtaining the figures in this form?

Shortly after working on these things, Pascal was out driving in a coach and four when the horses got out of hand. The two leading horses dashed over a bridge, and only the snapping of the traces saved his life. He believed that this was a special call for him to return to religion, and much of his remaining life was spent in or near a monastery.

In 1654 Pascal corresponded with his fellow countryman Fermat about the problem we have already mentioned, that of two players at a game of skill who wish to retire from the game before it is concluded. As stated, the two men agreed on the correct answer, though they had arrived at it by different means. Pascal worked out his solution by laying down some laws on the Theory of Probability.

His last work on mathematics was on the cycloid (see p. 117). Pascal solved several questions connected with this curve, some of which were achieved by the method of indivisibles, using an infinite number of points as part of a rather complicated calculation, again somewhat similar to the modern calculus.

It is said that he was suffering from a violent toothache when the subject occurred to him, and as he worked on it his toothache ceased. Regarding this as divine guidance, he worked on the geometry of the cycloid for eight days.

Pascal had always been rather delicate, and he so wore himself out by continual study that he died of sheer exhaustion when only 39.

7: WALLIS. 1616-1703

It seems strange to us these days that an English boy of fifteen who is attending school should have no knowledge at all of arithmetic, yet this was so in the case of John Wallis. When he was that age he happened to see a book of his brother's on the subject, was intrigued by the peculiar signs and symbols, borrowed the book and mastered its contents in a matter of days.

Though he was later sent to Cambridge to study as a doctor, his chief interest was still in mathematics, and it is rather amusing, in these circumstances, that he became a clergyman. However, he was later given a professorship in geometry at Oxford, where he lived until his death.

Wallis wrote on other things besides mathematics, including theology (the study of religion), logic (the science of reasoning), and philosophy (the study of reality, knowledge and existence); and he is said to have developed a method for teaching deaf and dumb people.

His mathematical writings are best known for their use of infinite series (that is, the use of series which continue without end), another forerunner of the calculus; and the ways in which he showed and explained the new methods in mathematics introduced by other writers. In 1655 Wallis published a work on conic sections in which he defined them analytically, that is, by means of an equation and two axes, but while the geometry of Descartes is involved and difficult to follow, that of Wallis is quite clear and straightforward, and it is the earliest work in which these curves are classified as being of the second degree.

His most important work is called *Arithmetica Infinitorum*, and in it he sets down in a methodical way the work of Descartes and another prominent mathematician called Cavalieri, in some cases even improving on it.

In this work also he proves the laws of indices. He shows that

x^0, x^{-1}, x^{-2}, represent 1, $\dfrac{1}{x}$, $\dfrac{1}{x^2}$, and that $x^{\frac{1}{2}}=\sqrt{x}$, $x^{\frac{2}{3}}=\sqrt[3]{x^2}$, and generally that x^{-n} (where n can be any number) represents the reciprocal of x^n. He then proceeds to find by a method of indivisibles (certain minute quantities) the area enclosed between particular curves. He failed, however, in his attempts to quadrate the circle (that is, if you remember, to find a square exactly equal to the area of a given circle) because he did not possess one of Newton's discoveries, the binomial theorem.

One of his interesting discoveries was the relationship that:

$$\frac{4}{\pi}=\frac{3\cdot3\cdot5\cdot5\cdot7\cdot7\quad\cdot\quad\cdot\quad\cdot}{2\cdot4\cdot4\cdot6\cdot6\cdot8\quad\cdot\quad\cdot\quad\cdot}$$

one of the earliest values of π found by such a means (known as infinite products).

Wallis also wrote two treatises (discussions), one on the cycloid and one on the cissoid (see pp. 117-18), which contained many new conclusions. He also made considerable investigations regarding centres of gravity, and produced works on the laws of motion, sound, astronomy, the tides and several other subjects. In addition, he was one of the first men to attempt to write a history of mathematics.

We could summarize the work of Wallis by saying that he recognized that the new (analytical) geometry was to replace the old (known as synthetic geometry) in higher mathematics, and that he contributed towards the invention of the infinitesimal calculus by his work on infinite series.

He is another mathematician who is said to have been a brilliant cryptologist, and to have helped the government in deciphering messages in code.

8: NEWTON. 1642-1727

THE story of the professor walking along the street who was so preoccupied looking up at the stars that he fell into a hole in the ground, is almost too old to be repeated. Yet these humorous accounts of absent-minded professors often have some truth in them, and the famous Isaac Newton was one who bore this out.

Several stories have been told about his absent-mindedness, many of them probably exaggerated, but two of them seem fairly established. One day he dismounted from his horse to lead it up a steep hill, but when he decided to remount at the top he found that he was left with only the horse's bridle, for the animal had slipped its harness and strolled off to graze. On another occasion he was entertaining some friends to dinner when he left the room to get a bottle of wine. After a long absence it was decided to see where he had gone, and he was found in his study working out a problem, completely forgetful of the fact that he was supposed to be entertaining friends.

In his early school life Isaac Newton did not seem to be very brilliant, but later he showed considerable ability and was sent to Cambridge, where he obtained a degree in 1665. This year, you may remember, was the year of the Great Plague, and as his college was closed down because of this, Newton returned to his home at Woolsthorpe in Lincolnshire. But he did not waste his time, for it was during this period that he began work on two of his greatest discoveries, the theory of universal gravitation and his fluxional calculus; for the latter, in particular, he used for the first time in a manuscript of 1665.

Newton's laws of gravitation state, among other things, that every particle of matter in the universe is attracting every other particle, and that the strength of the pull, or gravitation, of two bodies one upon the other depends in a definite way upon their mass and their distance apart. Also the attraction between two bodies is proportional to the masses multiplied together and then divided by the square of their distance apart. Thus, if the distance is doubled the attraction is reduced to one fourth. In this work Newton was aided by the findings of Copernicus and Kepler, and starting from the laws stated above he was able to give an explanation of numerous facts dealing with the heavenly bodies.

On returning to Cambridge in 1667 Newton took up a permanent post there, lecturing on several subjects, including optics (the science of light and vision) and algebra. In 1672 he astonished the scientific men of his time when he read to the Royal Society a paper on light and colour, in which he stated that white light was made up of the colours of the rainbow.

Four years after this he wrote an account of what is known as the binomial theorem, a formula by means of which a binomial quantity (an expression containing two terms) can be raised to a power without actual multiplication, or by which any root of it can be extracted by the use of a 'converging infinite series'.

In 1687, after having worked away for twenty years, Newton, though only after great persuasion, published his famous book known as the *Principia*. It was in three parts, and had a profound effect on scientific thought. The first part was on mechanics, and it contained theorems on motion. Part Two dealt with hydrodynamics, while Part Three which was called *System of the World* contained forty-two propositions on planets, comets and the moon. The whole book represents an amazing achievement, and it brought him great fame. He was later elected to parliament, made a knight, and from 1703 till his death in 1727 was re-elected president of the Royal Society every year.

As regards his work in mathematics, he published a work on algebra which contained the theory of equations. He also introduced the system of 'literal indices', such as a^m and a^n, and in analytic geometry he classified curves into 'algebraic' and 'transcendental', that is, capable or not capable of being produced by the usual operations of algebra. He also worked out an interpolation formula, by means of which it is possible to find terms in a series between any two non-consecutive terms.

Though he discovered many other things in algebra and physics, he is best remembered in mathematics for his invention of fluxions and fluents (see p. 135), which immediately preceded the modern infinitesimal calculus. The calculus is a part of modern mathematics which deals, among other things, with the rates of change of quantities which vary. If, for instance, we consider the circle, you know that as we change its radius so we change its area, and we thus say that the area of a circle is a function of its radius. The ratio of these rates of change is called the differential coefficient, and the means by which this ratio is worked out is called differentiation. If we wish to work the opposite way, that is, calculate the variable quantities from a knowledge of their rates of change, the process is called integration, and this method can deal with many other things, including the calculation of involved areas and volumes.

The differential and integral calculus together are known as the infinitesimal calculus. If you find all of this difficult to understand, you might simply remember that the calculus is that part of mathematics that deals with the rates of change of variable quantities.

Newton worked on his fluxional calculus, as it was called—because he used a notation of fluxions and fluents—long before any part of it was published, and he had previously communicated parts of it to other writers, including a German called Leibnitz. When this man later produced a calculus himself, a quarrel arose among mathematicians which has been called 'the most famous quarrel in the history of science', and we shall discuss it in the next chapter. All that we will say here is that Newton's methods later proved not quite so good as those of Leibnitz, but English mathematicians, sympathizing with Newton, kept to his notation for some time, and so slowed up the further development of mathematics in England for as long as they did this.

It is sometimes said that neither Newton nor Leibnitz invented a calculus as such; also, that nobody invented it, for it was the combined work of a group of men. This is partly true, for if you have understood the preceding chapters you will have seen that

Kepler, Fermat and Wallis all had similar ideas. The great contribution of Newton and Leibnitz was to show the usefulness of such methods and to demonstrate how they could be applied to other branches of science.

It is impossible to mention here all the subjects which this brilliant man investigated. He is sometimes referred to as a giant among tiny men. But he himself was modest, and he stated simply: 'If I have seen further than most men it is because I have stood on the shoulders of giants.'

He was great enough to realize that without Copernicus, Descartes, Kepler, Fermat, Wallis and others, there might never have been a Sir Isaac Newton as we now read of him.

When he died in 1727 he was buried in Westminster Abbey. The great French writer Voltaire attended the funeral. He was deeply moved. 'I have seen,' he said later, 'a professor of mathematics, only because he was great in his vocation, buried like a king who had done good to his subjects.'

9: LEIBNITZ. 1646-1716

THE father of Gottfried von Leibnitz was a professor at Leipzig in Germany, but he died when the boy was only six years old, and Gottfried was more or less obliged to look after his own education. He probably did it better than if he had been taught by tutors, for at eight he could read Latin, and at fifteen was well versed in logic (the science of reasoning). Two years later he went to a university, and at twenty was ready to take a degree in law, but though his knowledge was of the required standard the authorities refused to give the degree to one so young, so Leibnitz moved to another university where he was granted his degree and offered a professorship at the same time.

Leibnitz, however, turned this offer down, and instead took up service with one of the princes of Germany, whence he began to think and write about religion, politics and law. Later he visited Paris and became interested in mathematics, also writing a paper on the theory of combinations, and a description of a calculating machine more complicated than that of Pascal, for it would not only add and subtract, but would multiply and divide and even find square roots.

From Paris Leibnitz came to London, where he was made a member of the Royal Society and met several well-known English mathematicians, including Newton. When he finally arrived back in Germany he took up work as a librarian with another German ruler, and this man kept him busy on various schemes, but Leibnitz still managed to find time to pursue his studies, the most important of these being philosophy and mathematics.

He had a general idea of finding out the secrets of nature by co-operation amongst all nations, then of using this knowledge to enable all men to live in peace. In order to bring this about he tried to develop a universal language in which all nations could express their ideas freely, and it is said that his discoveries in connection with the infinitesimal calculus were connected with his investigation of symbols for use in this work.

His work on the calculus was published in 1684, but notes have been found in which he was using the method in 1675, though it was not properly developed by him for at least two years after this. Now the infinitesimal calculus, which has been mentioned on p. 132, can be expressed in a notation called fluxions, or in that of differentials. Newton's method was that of fluxions. If a changing quantity is represented by x, Newton denoted its rate of variation (called its fluxion) by $\dot{x}$, the fluxion of $\dot{x}$, or the second fluxion of x by $\ddot{x}$, and so on. Similarly, the variable quantity of a rate of change x (which he called its fluent) he showed by $\boxed{x}$, x', or $[x]$.

When Leibnitz set to work on problems requiring the use of a calculus, he invented a notation that was quite original and also much more useful for the further development of mathematics than that of Newton. He introduced the symbol 'd' (for differentiation) instead of the dot used by Newton, so that the rate of variation with his method would be denoted by 'dx'. Also, when adding up the variable quantities in integration he used the sign of an elongated 's' as $\int$, short for 'summa' and meaning the 'sum of' or 'integral of'.

It is known that Newton's method was set down before Leibnitz used his, and also that the latter saw some of Newton's papers soon after Newton first used his method. In view of this, and the fact of one or two subsequent alterations in his manuscripts—in one case an important date had been altered from 1675 to 1673—Leibnitz was accused of stealing Newton's ideas.

Now at the beginning of the 18th century, while both of these men were alive, either notation was satisfactory, for the applications of the calculus had not been fully worked out. In fact, the development of the infinitesimal calculus was the chief trend of mathematics during the following fifty years or so, and at the end of that time, about 1750, the differential notation of Leibnitz had shown itself to be superior to the fluxional notation of Newton; though sometimes the symbols $\dot{s}$ for the variation of distance with time (velocity) and s̈ for the variation of velocity with time (acceleration) are still used.

English mathematicians, convinced that Leibnitz had merely copied from Newton, were very bitter. They completely rejected the methods of Leibnitz in favour of those of Newton, so that for over a century mathematics progressed slowly in England compared with its development on the Continent, where the following was in favour of the work of Leibnitz.

The view generally held today is that Leibnitz had some idea of Newton's work on a calculus before he set to work on his own, and though the final results were similar, he proceeded along different lines from Newton, inventing a completely original symbolism. Therefore both he and Newton are entitled to credit for their respective discoveries.

Leibnitz also wrote a number of other works, particularly on mechanics and on certain involved curves, but some of these suggest that he did not have a thorough understanding of all that he wrote. The terms ordinate, co-ordinate and abscissa were first used by him, however, and after the name 'calculus integralis' had been suggested by the Swiss Jacques Bernoulli, Leibnitz adopted it in 1696.

Leibnitz was a prominent philosopher, and he holds an important place in the history of that science also. But as regards mathematics, his name with that of Newton will always be associated with the infinitesimal calculus, which has provided scientists with such a powerful means of attack on the involved problems which confront them from time to time.

The last few years of Leibnitz's life were rather distressing, owing to this great quarrel which raged unabated for some time. When he died at Hanover in 1716 he was almost penniless and unrecognized, and it is sad to read that his loyal secretary was the only one to mourn him, for his greatness was not fully understood until some years after his death.

10: MATHEMATICS AND MODERN SCIENCE

O u r story of elementary mathematics through the centuries is now finished. This is because almost all the mathematics that you have learnt at school so far was known, and was in its present form, by the end of the 17th century. This applies to arithmetic, algebra—whose symbolism has hardly changed—and elementary geometry. The only changes brought about are chiefly in the method of teaching these subjects. It does not matter, therefore, whether you merely glance through this chapter, or whether you discard it altogether.

It took over fifty years for the work of Newton to be fully understood and appreciated. In regard to the calculus of both him and Leibnitz, it was seen that once it had been improved upon it could be applied to a considerable number of subjects, and this was the chief development of the 18th and 19th centuries, in other words, in the field of higher mathematics.

The subject was now developing even more clearly into two main channels, the pure, confined to the subject itself and chiefly theoretical, and the applied, where it was being adapted to the many subjects which could be advanced by the use of its methods.

If you pursue your study of mathematics you may later come across such names as the Bernoulli brothers, Maclaurin, Simpson, Legendre, Gauss and others. We will mention only three others. Leonhard Euler, a Swiss, revised almost all the branches of pure mathematics, wrote important works on mathematical analysis, mechanics and astronomy, as well as writing one of the first complete textbooks on the differential calculus. Then there were the Frenchmen Lagrange, who developed the infinitesimal calculus and presented it in a form similar to that in use today, and Laplace, who added to the calculus, applied it to the theory of universal gravitation, and created a calculus of probabilities. Both of these men also applied mathematics to physical problems.

So mathematics grew into an essential part of any subject which could make use of its symbolism and its methods. We can illustrate this in the science of astronomy. In the middle of the 19th century astronomers were puzzled by the behaviour of the planet Uranus, which did not seem to be 'running to time' according to their very carefully calculated tables. When these were most studiously checked and found to be still in order, it was suggested that there might be another planet circling round the Sun beyond the orbit of Uranus which sometimes held it back and sometimes speeded it up. The only available method of verifying this theory was to calculate the position of this mysterious planet from the odd behaviour of Uranus.

This was done independently by an Englishman called Adams and a Frenchman named Leverrier. The answers of these men coincided, and when the astronomers directed their telescopes at the point indicated by their results, the 'new' planet, Neptune, was seen for the first time. A similar thing happened in 1930 when the ninth planet, Pluto, was discovered.

In the 19th century also, a theory of energy was being worked out whereby energy was divided into 'potential'—that which a body possesses by virtue of its position, such as a wound-up watch-spring—and 'kinetic'—that possessed by a body because of its motion, such as a moving bullet. A principle known as the 'conservation of energy' was also formulated, which stated that when a certain amount of energy disappears, an equal amount appears in another form. These researches finally led up to our recent discoveries, so that now terms like 'atomic power' and 'atomic energy' have passed into our everyday language and are being understood a little more by the average man.

Towards the end of the 19th century established ideas on matter were severely shaken when a new theory was put forward to the effect that a moving body contracts in the direction of its motion. This contraction is, of course, exceedingly minute even at tremendous speeds.

Could this same principle apply to that of time? Let us suppose, for example, that an instrument on the Earth is set to measure a time interval on some object that is moving away from the Earth at a tremendous speed. Would the time interval measured by the instrument on the Earth be any shorter than that measured by an instrument on the moving object? It should be, if the theory holds good.

Recently, nearly fifty years after it was first propounded, an experiment was conducted at Harwell Atomic Research Establishment in Berkshire with a specially-designed disc revolving about an electronic device, which proved that time as the scientist now measures it is relative to speed, and a film of this experiment was later shown to millions of viewers throughout the British Isles on their television screens.

Now when Isaac Newton worked out his theory of universal gravitation men felt that *the* system of the universe had been worked out at long last, but when these new conceptions seemed to be proved by Professor Einstein early in this century in his theory of Relativity, it was felt that Newton's ideas would have to be considerably altered. For the principles of Relativity satisfied several tests. They explained facts which otherwise would have remained unexplained, and predicted events which have since come to pass. It is now known that for bodies moving up to a few thousand miles per hour the laws of Newton are very nearly true, but for very high speeds the equations of Einstein must be employed.

Perhaps the most important idea proposed by Einstein was that mass could be converted into energy. If, for instance, one gramme of matter is destroyed—not merely changed to something else by burning, but completely destroyed—the energy set free would be equal to 25 million kilowatt hours. This fantastic truth, unhappily resulting in the atomic bomb as well as the atomic power station is expressed in Einstein's famous equation: $E = MC^2$; or, "available energy = mass destroyed × square of velocity of light".

Can you see now how far mathematics has progressed? Not only has it allowed our most outstanding men to attain their present level of academic knowledge, but it appears to be transcending the limitations of the human mind, and what the outcome of this will be, no one as yet can say.

Every young person today who takes an interest in topical affairs is bound to realize that we are seeing, in our day, far greater and more rapid changes than the world has ever known. Scientists are probing deeper and deeper into the secrets of life, of matter, of the universe; and most of their astounding discoveries depend, in the final analysis, upon the science of mathematics.

TYPICAL EXAMINATION QUESTIONS
BASED ON BOOK III

1. Write short notes on the Calculus.

2. Indicate the parts played in the development of mathematics by any two of the following:
   Kepler, Leibnitz, Pascal.

3. Explain, with particular reference to the work of some distinguished mathematicians of that century, why the 17th century is especially outstanding in the history of mathematics.

4. Write an essay on the great mathematicians of the 17th century.

5. Give the names and write a brief note about any mathematicians you would associate with the following:
   (a) The laws of planetary motion.
   (b) The law of gravitation.
   (c) Co-ordinate geometry.
   (d) The infinitesimal calculus.

6. Write an outline of the life of Sir Isaac Newton. Give a list of topics in which he made great advance and write brief notes on *one* of these.

7. With what development of notation in mathematics do you associate Leibnitz? Write a short account of his work in this connection.

8. What do you consider to be the greatest mathematical discovery of the 17th century? Give reasons for your answer.

9. Newton once said: 'If I have seen further than most men it is because I have stood on the shoulders of giants'. Say to whom you think he was referring and give reasons.

10. Write an essay on *one* of the following:
    (a) Galileo.
    (b) Descartes and the significance of his work.
    (c) Pascal.

Book Four

TOPICS OF PARTICULAR INTEREST

1: A BRIEF HISTORY OF ELEMENTARY ALGEBRA

T H E Ahmes Papyrus is the earliest known work to contain any algebraic problems, and it was written between 1650 and 1550 B.C. It deals with some simple numerical equations of the type $(x-1/7x=19)$, and the answers, given in unit fractions, are correct. Other Egyptian papyri contain problems involving both linear and quadratic equations, but no really good symbolism was used, and it is correct to say that algebra as a science did not exist in ancient Egypt.

The Babylonians showed a greater facility in algebra than the Egyptians, for clay tablets made in the reign of Hammurabi (about 1910 B.C.) show that these people could deal with quadratic, cubic, and even biquadratic equations, and had a vague knowledge of negative quantities. On some of these tablets, not only is the correct answer given, but also the method of solving the problem.

The ancient Greeks could solve algebraic problems of some difficulty, including those involving quadratic equations, but the answers were always worked out by means of geometry. The only Greek to write on algebra to any extent was the Alexandrian Diophantus, about A.D. 275. He was the first man to set down algebra in a book, to use a fairly consistent symbolism, and to solve problems, as we do, by means of analysis, some of them involving indeterminate equations. He is thus often called the 'father of algebra'.

There were four outstanding Hindu writers on algebra. These were Arya-Bhata, Brahmagupta, Mahavira and Bhaskara. Their work shows a considerable advance and includes work on series, permutations, and linear and quadratic equations, including a rule for solving the quadratic.

Under the great Arab conquests the work of the Greeks and that of the Hindus met, so that, particularly at Bagdad, such Arab writers as Alkarismi and Abu Kamil wrote excellent books on the subject. Alkarismi's work, especially, had a great influence on mathematics in Europe after it had been translated by Robert of Chester about 1140 and later writers.

The greatest writer on algebra in the Middle Ages was Fibonacci, who wrote two books on the subject dealing with several types of equations. Another Italian, Pacioli, wrote a work which summarized algebra as it was known up to his time, 1494, but the lack of a good symbolism prevented this from being a clear exposition of the subject.

The invention of printing helped in the development of algebra, and the first important work to appear in print was by another Italian, Cardan, in a work called *Ars Magna* (1545). This contained the solution of the cubic and biquadratic equations, and is looked upon as the first real progress towards modern algebra. But not all of this was Cardan's own work, for the cubic equation he had obtained from one of his colleagues called Tartaglia under a promise not to divulge it, and the biquadratic was the work of one of his pupils called Ferrari.

When the first Italian textbook bearing the name of algebra was printed in 1572 by Bombelli, it was so systematically arranged that all that was needed was to develop a good symbolism. This was worked out in the next one hundred years, so that by the end of the 17th century elementary algebra was much as it is today. We will now briefly discuss how this symbolism came about.

The Development of Notation in Algebra

Though you have read that the earliest use of symbols is in the Ahmes Papyrus, where addition and subtraction are indicated by two legs walking forwards and backwards respectively, something like this $\wedge$ and $\wedge$, it was really a written form of hieroglyphics and as such could not properly be known as symbols. Though we will include the symbolism of Diophantus in the work below, it should be remembered that the earliest copy we have of his manuscript was written in the 13th century, and is therefore not completely reliable.

Addition

Diophantus and the later Greeks, as well as the Hindus, indicated addition by juxtaposition, or, if you like, 'placing next to'. Our present method in arithmetic is really based on this, as when we write $2\frac{1}{2}$ for 2 plus $\frac{1}{2}$.

It is quite possible that the origin of the present sign, as of that for minus, can be traced back to the early days of mercantile arithmetic, when the merchants marked sacks or wooden chests full of goods with a plus or minus sign to indicate that they were over or under weight. A *Mercantile Arithmetic* written by a German called Widman in 1489 seems to bear this out. For a long time the symbols were used in arithmetic in the same way, that is, not to indicate an operation, but merely excess or deficiency.

In algebra the earlier Italians wrote 'plus' in full, short for 'surplus', and later contracted this to 'P' or 'p', drawing a line through the letter to show that it was a symbol and not a quantity. Sometimes the operation of addition was shown by a bar as $\bar{p}$, or by the sign ø.

One of the first to use the sign in algebra appears to have been a Dutchman called Hoecke, in 1514, and soon after this the sign made an appearance in the mathematical works of Germany. Stifel did as much as anyone to bring the sign into general use as a symbol of operation, together with that of minus, and Robert Recorde introduced the two signs into England about 1542, though as symbols of operation they were confined to algebra.

Subtraction

Diophantus indicated subtraction by the sign Λ, which may have been a sign of negation turned upside down, or a deformed L, the initial for a word indicating subtraction.

The Hindus often showed subtraction by a small circle or a dot placed above the quantity to be subtracted as in $\overset{\circ}{5}$ or $\overset{\cdot}{5}$, or sometimes the quantity, called the subtrahend, was enclosed in a circle as ⑤.

The development of our present minus sign is similar to that of our plus sign, being used, as stated, in medieval warehouses to indicate a deficiency in weight, and as the Italian algebraists denoted 'p' for plus, so they wrote 'M' or 'm' for minus, a line being drawn through the letter as before, or a bar being written over it, as $\overline{m}$. Again, to Stifel and Recorde goes the credit for bringing the symbol into general use in Germany and England respectively.

Multiplication

The symbol for multiplication developed more slowly than that for plus and minus, because of the popularity of the two latter as warehouse signs. Slight variations of it had been in use in arithmetic to denote a cross multiplication and similar operations, but an English clergyman, William Oughtred, first used it in its present form as a symbol of operation in 1631. Because it was so liable to be confused with the letter x in algebra, the symbol was not very popular. Often a dot was used instead, as $2 \cdot 4 = 8$, or $2.4 = 8$. Leibnitz was one of the first writers to make a general use of this method, though he also used the symbol $\frown$.

Division

Our present symbol for division, it may surprise you to know, is used on the Continent to indicate a subtraction. The Arabs denoted division in one of three ways, 6–3, or 6/3, or $\frac{6}{3}$. Oughtred introduced the colon (:) to show a ratio between quantities in 1657, and it may well be that our present symbol for division is the combination of the ratio and minus signs; it was first used in England by John Pell in 1668. The symbol itself was not a new one, for in the 15th century it was used by Italian merchants to indicate one half, as in $3 \div$ or $3 \div$ ($3\frac{1}{2}$).

Equality

The symbol we now use for equality was introduced by Robert Recorde about 1557 (see p. 89), but two vertical parallel lines, as ||, were also used. Neither of these signs was very popular, however, and until 1600 the word 'aequalis' was written in full. After this and until the time of Newton, it was usual to write ∞ or ∝, being a contraction of the first two letters of 'aequalis'.

Power

Diophantus, about whom we read on pp. 57-9, called the third power a 'cube', the fourth power a 'power-power', the fifth power a 'power-cube' and so on. The next earliest attempt was by the Italian Bombelli who, when using ① for the unknown, used ②ʲ for its square, ③ʲ for its cube and so on, but Vieta improved on this with his A quadratus, or A quad., A cubus, or A cub., etc.

Descartes used our present method of exponents to show the power to which a quantity was raised, but his indices were only positive whole numbers, and it was left to John Wallis to explain what negative and fractional indices, such as x^{-2} and $x^{\frac{1}{2}}$, really meant. To Isaac Newton is usually given the credit for introducing a^n and so on, indicating a power of any magnitude.

Radical, or Root, Sign

Early writers often set down the word for root or side when indicating a square or other root, while the symbol most frequently used by medieval writers was ℞, short for 'radix'. The first appearance of the symbol $\sqrt{}$ in print was in Rudolff's *Cos* in 1525, but he did not use any indices, and when Stifel rewrote this work he set down ₂/ for $\sqrt{}$, ₃/ for $\sqrt[3]{}$, and ₄/ for $\sqrt[4]{}$. Bhaskara, however, used a somewhat similar sign in the 12th century, and this is said to be the only operative symbol translated from the Hindu by the Arabs, so that they also must have been aware of it.

Even after Stifel's work there were still many variations of methods for indicating a root, but later Newton used $\sqrt{\frac{3}{8}}$ and

$\sqrt{\frac{4}{16}}$ for $\sqrt[3]{8}$ and $\sqrt[4]{16}$, as well as our present method, so that by the end of the 17th century it was being written in a similar way to our way of writing roots today.

Other Symbols

The symbols above are usually classed as the most important in the development of elementary algebra. The remaining symbols, such as the vinculum (the line written above a number of terms), brackets, and the signs for inequality have little history attached to them.

The vinculum was first used by Vieta in 1591, brackets by Girard in 1629, and the signs > for 'is greater than' and < for 'is less than', by Harriot in 1631.

2: A SHORT ACCOUNT OF THE DEVELOPMENT OF ELEMENTARY TRIGONOMETRY

I T would seem that the Egyptians were the first people to know of the fixed ratios of similar triangles, for in the Ahmes Papyrus there are five problems dealing with the mensuration of pyramids, and four of these use the term 'seqt' of an angle. Though the meaning of this term is rather vague in the text, it is possible that it referred to the cosine or the cotangent of the angle of the side of a pyramid and its base. Other than this, there is nothing to show that they had any knowledge of the subject, nor is there any record of any tables having been compiled.

Through communications with Egypt, the Babylonians may have had a similar vague notion of trigonometry, for they showed some knowledge of angle measurement in very early times, but little about this is definitely known.

You have previously read about the measurement of the pyramid by Thales, and though he might have done this by means of finding a tangent to A in the sketch, it is almost certain that he did it by means of: CA : CD=BA : BE.

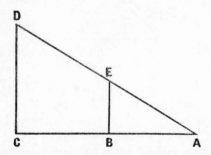

The Greek Aristarchus of Samos, who lived about 260 B.C., made an important advance in the progress of trigonometry when he tried to measure the diameters of the Sun and Moon, and to find their distances from the earth. If you look at the sketch below you will see that he chose the time of the half moon for his calculations in regard to the latter, and his proof indicates ratios suggesting the tangent of an angle, so that his method may have been something like this, except that 'A' is diminished:

1.

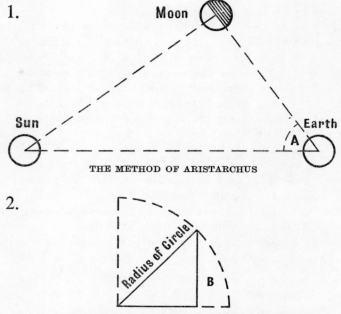

THE METHOD OF ARISTARCHUS

2.

THE USE OF THE CHORD IN TRIGONOMETRY.
B IS A HALF-CHORD.

Of course his instruments were very crude, though his reasoning was quite sound, but the nearest he could get to the Moon's distance as a ratio of the Sun's was between 1/18 and 1/20. Nevertheless, it was a very original method.

As a sound system, trigonometry may have begun with the works of the Greek Hipparchus (about 140 B.C.), who is said to have written twelve books with tables called *On Chords of Circles*, but unfortunately all of these have been lost. Hipparchus and other Greeks usually solved a problem on a triangle by inscribing it in a circle so that the sides of the triangle became chords, and a table of chords would be of great use with such a method. You may understand the use of a chord in this way by referring to sketch 2 opposite.

Astronomy was the greatest influence in the development of trigonometry, and we find that all those who made any contribution to the science right up to the middle of the 15th century did so as a result of astronomical studies. Often their work referred to spherical triangles, that is, triangles based on the surface of a sphere, but we shall confine this chapter mostly to plane trigonometry.

An astronomer named Menelaus of Alexandria, for instance, wrote six books on chords which, again, are lost, but his work on spherical triangles is one of the oldest known, and in it he proves two relationships concerning the plane triangle and two concerning the spherical triangle.

Ptolemy, who lived about A.D. 150, helped the subject when he summarized the theorems of Hipparchus, and though he also used chords of angles instead of sines, he had some idea of the sine, and it may be that the Hindus obtained some knowledge of sines from his work, called the *Almagest*.

When the Hindus set down their tables they used half-chords, which is what we call sines today, and these appear in the writings of Aryabhata (about A.D. 500), a work which shows some knowledge of the functions of angles. The work of later Hindus was mostly the setting down of tables of sines of remarkable accuracy, and all this was passed on to the Arabs, one of whom, Al Battam (about 900), gave names to the functions of cotangent and secant, though he did not call them this.

About 1250 a Persian astronomer, Nasir al-Tusi, collected all the known knowledge of trigonometry, added parts to it, and set it all down into a complete work, the first time in which plane geometry is regarded as a science in itself. He uses the sine theorem, but as there was no cosine theorem at his time he solved oblique triangles by means of auxiliary right-angled triangles.

In Europe trigonometry developed more in Spain as a result of work in astronomy. About 1050 sets of tables were constructed, to be so improved upon in the 12th and 13th centuries that they were used by astronomers over a very long period. Fibonacci was also acquainted with the subject from his knowledge of Arab works, and he applied it to surveying.

By the 15th century Europe was becoming well acquainted with the subject, and a German, Johann Muller, better known as Regiomontanus, was the first modern writer to establish trigonometry as a separate science from astronomy, about 1460. He worked out new tables, possibly invented the tangent, and so set the subject down that it could develop much more quickly. Copernicus, the famous astronomer, added to the work of Regiomontanus and introduced the secant about 1560.

Vieta, who is best known for his work in notation in algebra, helped in the analytical treatment of trigonometry, that is, solving problems by means of equations, and he also worked out the sine of 1′ to thirteen figures, which he used for the basis of his tables. He was also the first to use systematically all the six functions, writing out the cosine formula for solving triangles in complete form, and re-stating the tangent formula much as it is today.

The formula for finding the angle direct from the sides without using auxiliary right-angled triangles was first published by a man called Rhaeticus of Wittenburg about 1596, but his tables were corrected by Pitiscus, another German, who used the word 'trigonometry' for the first time as the title of his book.

3: THE HISTORY OF Π

O F all the terms and quantities used in mathematics, that known as Pi or π is perhaps the most famous. It is known as the ratio of the circumference of a circle to its diameter, and in this chapter we shall refer to it mostly as 'ratio', but in higher mathematics π is also used in problems not obviously connected in any way with the circle.

Mensuration, as we have seen, played an important part in early mathematics, and the simple figure of the circle was one which interested the ancient peoples. As they investigated its properties in the course of time, they became aware of the strange relationship between the circumference and the diameter and tried to estimate it.

The Babylonians estimated this relationship as 3, and though in future we shall refer to the relationship as pi or π, you must try to bear in mind that our present symbol was not introduced until just over two hundred years ago. This value of pi was, of course, quite sufficient for the purposes of the Babylonians, and it is interesting to note that the Jews used this value also, as you will read by looking up I Kings vii. 23 in the Bible.

The earliest known trace of an approximate value for pi is in the Ahmes Papyrus, written about the 16th century B.C. It is a problem on the area of a circle of diameter 12, no unit of length being given, and in our modern symbols the form would be:

$$A = (D - \tfrac{1}{9}D)^2$$

which gives π a value of 3·1605, an answer probably arrived at through long experience.

Archimedes, who lived about 225 B.C., was the next person to make an outstanding contribution to the value. In his *Measure of the Circle* he sets down three propositions:

(1) The area of a circle is the same as that of a right-angled triangle, the sides forming the right angle being equal to

the radius and the circumference. (If $R = Radius$, this means that the area $= \frac{1}{2}R(2\pi R)$.

(2) The ratio of the area of a circle to the square on the diameter is nearly 11 : 14. (In other words, $\pi R^2 : (2R)^2 = 11 : 14$.)

(3) The ratio of the circumference of a circle to its diameter is less than $3\frac{1}{7}$ but more than $3\frac{10}{71}$.

To demonstrate propositions (2) and (3) Archimedes inscribed in and circumscribed about a circle regular polygons of 96 sides, calculated their perimeters, and assumed the circumference to lie between them. If our present method of finding square roots had been known, his answers would have been even more nearly accurate.

Ptolemy of Alexandria, who lived about 150 B.C., in his sixth book on the Theory of Eclipses, gives the value of the ratio as $3° \ 8' \ 30''$. This really means $3\frac{17}{120}$, and if you care to work this out you will find that it comes to $3 \cdot 141\dot{6}$.

This close value of π was, however, generally overlooked, and the value of Archimedes—$3\frac{1}{7}$—became recognized as a satisfactory approximation. Even the Romans were not concerned with great accuracy in these matters, and so one Roman called Vitruvius said, about 20 B.C., that the circumference of a wheel of diameter 4 feet is $12\frac{1}{2}$ feet, thus using the ratio of $3\frac{1}{8}$.

Apart from the far East, the Hindus were the next people to make some contribution to the value, though the estimation of the prominent writers often varied. Aryabhata, in working out a table of sines about A.D. 500, used $3 \cdot 1416$. His rule is quite interesting, and reads somewhat as follows:

'Add 4 to 100, multiply by 8, add 62,000; the result is the approximate value of the circle when the diameter is 20,000.'

This makes π equivalent to $\frac{62832}{20000}$, or $3 \cdot 1416$.

A few years after this, Brahmagupta used 3 as a 'practical value' and $\sqrt{10}$ as a 'neat value'. Since with the common approximation of square roots in the Middle Ages, $\sqrt{10}$ would be $3\frac{1}{7}$, after this time $\sqrt{10}$ became recognized as the value of π throughout the East and in medieval Europe.

Though in this work we have purposely not dealt with China, it is worth mentioning that the Chinese had many values for

π, but their methods of working these out are not known. 3 was used before 1,000 B.C., then later $\sqrt{10}$—even before Brahmagupta —then about A.D. 265 $\frac{142}{45}$ was in use, making the value 3·1555. One Chinese called Liu Hiu gives some idea of one method in use. He begins, as Archimedes did, with a regular inscribed hexagon, then doubles the number of sides repeatedly, and he says that if this is continued till it can be done no more, the perimeter of the figure finally agrees with the circle.

Another Chinese, Tsu Chung-Chih, who lived about 470, started with a circle of 10 ft. diameter and finally obtained 3·1415927 and 3·1415926 as the limits of π. This was an amazing calculation, and no closer approximation was made for a thousand years. The same man stated that $\frac{355}{113}$ was the 'accurate value' and $\frac{22}{7}$ the 'neat value'.

From the 11th to the 19th century various close approximations of π were calculated, and in particular an Arab called Al Kashi, about 1430, wrote down the value as:

sah-sah

3   141592653898732   !

There is no need for you to try to remember all these figures, but this was the highest degree of accuracy up to his time and for the next one hundred years.

Vieta also made a useful attempt at the value when he calculated the limits to the tenth decimal place, then after his time π was calculated to rather ridiculous limits by various mathematicians, to 140, then 200, then 500 decimal places, and in 1853 William Shanks actually carried the value to 707 decimal places!

As regards the symbol itself, Oughtred used $\dfrac{\delta}{\pi}$ in 1647 to represent the ratio of the diameter to the circumference, and David Gregory some fifty years later used $\dfrac{\pi}{P}$ for the ratio of the circumference to the radius.

William Jones is usually recognized as being the first man to use π definitely in its present relationship, and when Leonhard Euler, the Swiss, used it in 1737 it came into general use.

4: A SHORT ACCOUNT OF CALCULATING DEVICES

I F we wish to be precise, we could say that the first device used for calculation is the same as that used by younger children, the fingers, and it is not surprising to learn that some primitive tribes still calculate in this way. Indeed, some of these tribes have no special word for any number higher than 10, so that any quantity above 10 is referred to as 'plenty' or 'heap'.

Because of the difficulty of counting in such numbers, many tribes would get two men to stand together, and while one of them would count in units up to 10, the other kept a record of the number of 10's on his fingers. Some tribes are even known to have used their toes for keeping this record of 10's.

After a period of time it was noticed by the more forward tribes that numbers could be represented by means of pebbles or sticks arranged in groups of 10, and this eventually led up to the invention of the dust table. On a flat slab covered with sand or dust, marks were made by means of a piece of wood or similar object, and when no longer required these lines were rubbed out with the finger.

After a further long period, the next step in progress appears to have been a table ruled with lines, and small objects were placed on these lines to indicate numbers. This form of calculating device was in use for hundreds of years, up to the 16th century in parts of Europe, and even later in some parts of the world.

As time went on, a further type evolved. This was a slab or table either grooved or arranged with rods, and movable discs or balls were used in the grooves or on the rods. This was the most popular type, and is even in use today in the eastern world.

This, then, was the gradual evolution of the counting frame, the general name for which is 'abacus'. First came the dust table, then the lined table, and then the table marked with grooves or arranged with rods, discs or counters being used in connection with the last two. We will now discuss some of the variations to these types.

ROMAN ABACUS

As you have read, the Romans did most of their calculations by means of the abacus, recording the results in their well-known numerals. Their calculating frames or tables often had two extra grooves or wires, one of which held four counters and the other twelve to help with the calculation of quarters and twelfths. Other than this, the Roman abaci were similar to previous ones, the first groove or wire after the 'fractional' ones representing units, the next tens, the next hundreds, and the fourth thousands.

In China such a device for calculating is known as the 'Suan-Pan', and because of this the abacus is often referred to as the 'swan pan'.

GERBERT'S ABACUS

About the year A.D. 970 a Frenchman named Gerbert went to Spain to study Arabic numerals. He later proved himself a remarkable scholar and eventually rose to the high office of Pope of Rome. But he is also credited with the invention of a column counting frame, named 'Gerbert's Abacus' after him. The main advance was to use counters marked with the numbers they were supposed to represent, rather than the required number of single counters—a counter marked with a 6, for instance, would be used instead of six counters. But this was not too great an advantage, for the time saved in manipulating the counters was often lost by having to find just the right counter, and in addition some ability was necessary for learning certain tables of numbers.

On this type of abacus lines were drawn on the board or table and over every three lines was drawn an arc to help with the calculations, so that this type was also known as the 'arc abacus'. It looked something like this:

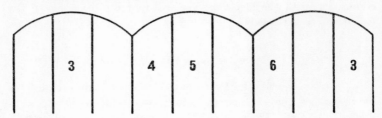

As you can guess, the number shown here is 30,450,603.

LINE ABACUS

This abacus, based on the decimal system like the previous one, was made up of a number of lines drawn horizontally on a table, each line standing for an order of ten. It was the most common type of abacus in western Europe, and in England it was known as the counting table. It was based on the following principle:

———————————————	10,000's
	5,000's
———×————————⊖——	1,000's
	500's
	100's
	50's
	10's
	5's
	Units

As you can see, counters were placed on the lines and in the spaces between the lines, the rule being that there must not be more than four counters on a line or more than one counter in

the space between the lines. When during the course of calculations five counters appeared on a line, one was carried to the
space above, and from this our expression 'to carry', which we
use in addition, is believed to have its origin. You will notice the
cross on the fourth line. This was to help the eye when reading
the numbers, and another cross would be placed on the millions
line. Again, our system of using commas to separate the groups
of thousands is said to have originated from this line abacus.

The number indicated on the line abacus opposite is 1,862, and
here is a sum as it might appear on the complete line abacus
with its answer.

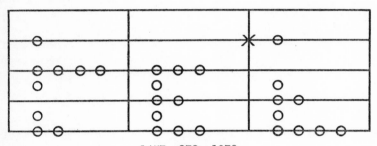

1457 — 378 = 1079

In England there is little real evidence to show the methods
of reckoning used up to the time of the Middle Ages, but it
is possible that the methods may have been like those of the
Romans. We do know that about the 13th century the lines or
columns on the abacus had changed from the vertical position to
the horizontal, but just when this change took place is not known.

The merchants and others dealing with money calculations
sat on benches with chequered boards, usually of black and
white squares, before them, and on these chequered boards or
tables were placed the discs or 'counters'. In time this chequered
board became the symbol of a money changer, and as money
transactions were often carried out in inns, it became the symbol
for an inn also. As taxes due to the king were paid in and reckoned
up under this system as well, the receiving house became known
as the Court of the Exchequer, which is also the reason that the

man now in charge of the country's finances is known as the Chancellor of the Exchequer.

OTHER METHODS USED

Tally

Though not actually used for calculations, but rather as a means of keeping accounts, the tally is worth mentioning here. It was a piece of wood on which scores (or 'scars') were cut. Almost any amount of money could be indicated by means of the position and size of the notches, £100 by the width of the thumb, £20 by the width of the finger, £1 by the breadth of a barley corn. Smaller amounts were usually scratched on the wood at one end. The tally was then split lengthwise so that each person, the one making a payment and the one receiving it, kept a part. From this comes the term 'The accounts tally'.

Knotted Cords

Also used for keeping a record of numbers was the string of knotted cords. Such a method is mentioned several times throughout history in various lands, and is still used by natives in some parts of the world. As it is not used in actual calculation, we do no more than merely mention it here, but it is quite possible that the rosary used by Roman Catholics had its origin from this source.

Finger Computation

As was stated at the beginning of this chapter, finger notation was carried on by most early peoples, and came down through the ages. In time a system was developed whereby the left hand was used for numbers up to one hundred, and the right hand for hundreds. This method of indicating numbers was found most useful for bargaining at international fairs, where the different languages used and the lack of an otherwise consistent notation hampered the exchange of goods or money.

From finger notation developed finger reckoning or computation. By this means not only simple calculations such as addition could be performed, but also multiplication. The system is too detailed to describe here, but it is very similar to the method used by deaf and dumb people.

MODERN CALCULATING METHODS

Napier's Rods or Bones

After the abacus the next important development in mechanical means of calculation was that introduced by the founder of modern logarithms, John Napier, in 1617. He arranged a series of rods as you see here:

1	2	3	4	5	6	7	8	9	0
/2	/4	/6	/8	1/0	1/2	1/4	1/6	1/8	/0
/3	/6	/9	1/2	1/5	1/8	2/1	2/4	2/7	/0
/4	/8	1/2	1/6	2/0	2/4	2/8	3/2	3/6	/0
/5	1/0	1/5	2/0	2/5	3/0	3/5	4/0	4/5	/0
/6	1/2	1/8	2/4	3/0	3/6	4/2	4/8	5/4	/0
/7	1/4	2/1	2/8	3/5	4/2	4/9	5/6	6/3	/0
/8	1/6	2/4	3/2	4/0	4/8	5/6	6/4	7/2	/0
/9	1/8	2/7	3/6	4/5	5/4	6/3	7/2	8/1	/0

Fig. 1. Napier's Rods or Bones

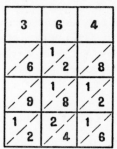

Fig. 2. Method of Use

The strips were numbered at the top from 1 to 0, and in the eight divisions below each figure was successively multiplied by 2, 3, 4, etc., the tens being separated from the units by an oblique line.

Fig. 2 shows the method of multiplying. Suppose it is required to multiply 364 by 4. The columns headed 3 and 6 and 4 are selected and placed side by side in that order. As the multiplier is 4, the fourth line is read off by adding the numbers between the oblique parallel lines, which, if you refer again to Fig. 2, becomes 1,456—the correct answer. It should be pointed out that the strips run longitudinally. Fig. 2 is merely a diagram to avoid confusion, and the figures that would normally appear below row 4 are not shown.

These rods were extremely popular, not only in Europe but even in China and Japan, and for many years they occupied an important place in mathematics. As you might guess, they could also be used for division, though the procedure was a little less straightforward.

Modern Machines

When we come to modern calculating machines the underlying principle is that all carrying is done by the machine. This is achieved by means of discs, so arranged that the first has to turn ten units before it revolves the second one unit and so on.

The first invention of such a machine is credited to Pascal, who made one in 1642 when only 19 years of age. Then in 1673 an Englishman named Morland invented one that would multiply, while Leibnitz is said to have invented one about the same time that would also divide. It was not, however, until the 19th century that machines were made to perform the four operations successfully.

Since 1892 machines have been made which will also print the figures and their totals. Such machines are now becoming quite commonplace, not only in banks and offices but even in retail stores. Some machines can carry out any form of reckoning merely by the touch of the correct button.

Before we conclude this section we should just mention the latest device of all. This is commonly called the 'electronic brain'. It is a most complicated arrangement, consisting of numerous valves and electric circuits which, used in the first place as a scientist's plaything, can now be adapted to almost any use including that of operating other machines. The most complicated electronic brain is able to solve in a few minutes equations which would take the most brilliant scientist several months, if not years.

The Slide Rule

An ingenious device which has recently come into even greater use is the slide rule. Edmund Gunter was one of the first to work

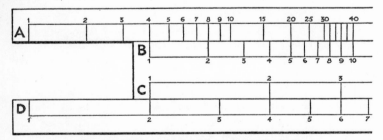

SIMPLIFIED DIAGRAM OF THE SLIDE RULE

The slide is set for multiplication or division by 4. For a description of the method see p. 164.

on this idea when he designed a 'logarithmic line of numbers' called Gunter's Scale in 1620. With the aid of compasses it was possible to perform the operations of multiplication and division on this scale. About two years later Oughtred also invented a logarithmic rule, but in 1654 Robert Bissaker made a slide rule very much like those in use today.

From that time other improvements were introduced, such as increasing the scales without enlarging the instrument, and adapting it for use in special branches of science.

The simple slide rule has a slide which moves in a groove cut in the body of the rule. Scales are marked on both edges of the slot of the rule, and similar scales are marked on the slide. The scales are graduated in proportion to the logarithm of the numbers shown on them, so that the distance from the first mark to any subsequent mark is in proportion to the logarithm of the number shown at the subsequent point.

The principle of the scale rule is therefore similar to that of working with logarithms. In multiplication, for instance, the logarithms of the two numbers are really added by moving the slide to the appropriate position, but as the scales are marked, not with the logarithms, but with the figures corresponding to them, the answer can be read direct from the rule.

To multiply 4 by 8, as a simple example, the first mark of the scale on the slide is set against the 4 on the rule, as in the diagram on p. 163, and the answer is found by going along the slide to the 8 on row B, and reading off the number set against this mark on the scale of the rule, that is, row A.

The principle of division is something like the reverse process, for the distances corresponding to the two logarithms of the numbers are subtracted one from the other. To carry out division the two numbers involved are set against each other, the divisor on the slide and the dividend on the rule. The answer is found by going along to the first mark on the slide, B 1 in the diagram, and reading off the number on the scale of the rule, row A, against which this index mark is set.

The unit length of the top scales on both the rule and the slide is made one half of the bottom scales on both rule and slide. By this means it is possible to obtain the square roots and the squares of numbers.

Thus by means of the scale rule, the operations of multiplication, division, the finding of square roots and the squaring of numbers can be speedily accomplished.

5: THE DEVELOPMENT OF OUR CALENDAR

It is believed that the Sumerians established a calendar as early as 4700 B.C., for observations of the heavens made them aware of the changes of the Moon, and also that these changes took place during the return of the seasons. The Sumerian scribe therefore began a new month with every new Moon, making up his year of twelve such months and slipping in an extra month when his year was nearly that amount of time ahead of the seasons. The years were not numbered, but were named after some important event in the year, as was the custom in Egypt.

The Babylonians were the first real astronomers, making scientific observations within their limited means as early as 2200 B.C., and like the Sumerians, they made their year one of 360 days. We learn that in Hammurabi's reign the calendar had moved forward a whole month in front of spring, and as the sheep shearing at this time was regarded as a kind of feast, the king sent a letter to all his governors saying: 'Since the year hath a deficiency, let the month which is now beginning be registered as a second month of Elul.'

About 750 B.C. the skies were being continually observed and records were kept of these observations, so that by 500 B.C. a Chaldean astronomer named Nabu-Rimannu was able to work out tables of the motions of the Sun and Moon, giving the times of these bodies to make their revolutions. He also calculated the year as 365 days, 6 hours, 15 minutes and 41 seconds, the earliest known close approximation, being only 26 minutes 55 seconds in excess.

About a hundred years after this another Chaldean called

Kidinnu made a similar group of tables, which are so accurate that parts of them have been used in astronomical calculations by modern astronomers.

EGYPT

The Egyptian calendar differed from the Babylonian inasmuch as it was based not on the Moon (lunar) but on the Sun (solar). This was in the first place by reason of observations on the flooding of the Nile. In order to be able to assess before the harvest the amount of taxes to be paid, the king's officials measured and recorded the height of the Nile floods. By studying these records they found that over a period of fifty years the average interval between the floods was 365 days to the nearest day. Bearing this in mind they established an official calendar to help with farming the land. After a long period the difference of six hours in each year became quite obvious, but the Egyptians preferred not to make any alterations in this direction.

About 4000 B.C. the observations on the stars showed the star we now call Sirius rising just before the Sun in the latitude of Cairo. This always occurred just before the flooding of the Nile, and so became a warning of the rising of the river. As the rising of Sirius was easy to observe, the day of its first appearance was called New Year's Day, and as the lunar months already in use would not fit into this period, they made their months each of thirty days, and added five more days to the end of the year as a kind of holiday, and this proved an extremely convenient arrangement. It is believed that the introduction of this calendar took place in 4236 B.C., the earliest dated event in all history.

The act of adding these five days to the last month of the year (known as Mesori), still did not take into account the six hours or quarter of a day by which the year was short, so their year became a changing one, coming back to where it started every 1,460 years.

The Egyptians divided their year into three seasons, the 'Inundation' or the flooding, the 'Coming Forth' or the freeing of the fields from the floods, and the 'Harvest'. These seasons

M

were determined by the scribes in the temples, who were able to prophesy the coming of the 'Inundation' by means of cleverly concealed Nilometers which, through the communicating underground channels that had been made, showed the slightest rise in the level of the water.

The months in the year of this calendar were numbered, but the years themselves were given names, usually after some important event that had happened during the year, and lists of year names were also kept for reference and have been found invaluable by historians. Later the Egyptians numbered the years of each king's reign and dated events as 'the sixth year in the reign of King Akhenaton' and so on.

GREEKS

Though the Greeks inherited the astronomical tables of the Babylonians, the calendar in use at Athens followed that of Egypt, by beginning a new day at sunset and dividing both day and night into twelve hours. They did not use the seven-day week, however, but divided their month into three parts, one of ten days, one of nine days, and the third with the number of days left over in the month, which varied. Twelve of these months made up 354 days, which required a new month every three years.

ROMANS

The calendar of the early Romans consisted of only ten months, and to this were later added, about 700 B.C., the months of January and February. This year was a lunar one, but about the 5th century B.C. a solar year was introduced, the priests being left to work this out. However, they appear to have made such a poor attempt at it, that it was 80 days out by the time of Julius Caesar, about 50 B.C.

To try to put things right Caesar ordered that the year 46 B.C. should consist of 445 days, and that after this date every year should be of 365 days with a leap year every fourth year. His calendar began with March, so that September, October, November and December were the seventh, eighth, ninth and tenth months respectively, hence their names. Every alternate month had 31 days and the others 30 days, with the exception of February, which received its thirtieth day once in every four years.

Caesar later ordered that the year should begin with January followed by February, and the month called Quintilis, originally the fifth, was renamed July after him. He also rearranged the days of the months as they are today. Unfortunately, in the second year of this calendar the priests were again confused, this time over which year should be the leap year. As Caesar was now dead, the Emperor Augustus settled the matter, and probably as Caesar had named a month after himself, so Augustus changed Sextilis to August.

GREGORIAN

From this time the Julian calendar, as it was called, remained in operation until 1582. Then, as the calendar had fallen back one day in every 128 years, the Easter festival was nearly a fortnight out. After discussing the problem with scientists Pope Gregory XIII ordered that 4 October 1582 should become 15 October, and that three leap years should be dropped every 400 years. This was set down in a simple way by stating that every year ending in 100 should not be a leap year, unless the number of the year is divisible by 400. Thus the year 1900 was not a leap year, but the year 2000 will be. This arrangement of the calendar needs no further adjustment for 3,000 years. This new calendar known as the Gregorian calendar, was adopted by various countries during the next two hundred years, and by England in 1752.

No mention has been made of the numbering of **our** years This actually took place about A.D. 900, when Christians decided to count the years forwards and backwards from the birth of Christ. It is now believed that Christ was born not in A.D. 1 but about 4 B.C., but by the time this estimation came to light it was **much** too late to make any alteration **in** the present numbering.

6: METHODS OF RECORDING TIME

SUNDIALS

I T is quite likely that early man noticed that the shadows cast by rocks or trees were roughly in the same place at the same time each day. At first he probably set stones to mark various times around the tip of the shadow cast by the object, and so constructed a primitive sundial. He may also have marked a period of time by means of two stones, indicating when he would set out and when he might be expected to return from his hunting or some other journey.

In time an artificial object was set up, more correctly called a gnomon, and since it was seen that the length of the shadow varies according to the angle of the sun above the horizon, curved lines were drawn around the gnomon or a hollow surface was made.

The earliest mention of a sundial is found in the Book of Isaiah, about 700 B.C., but the idea was very old even then, for an Egyptian sun clock dated at about 1500 B.C. has been reconstructed in Berlin museum, and it looks something like this:

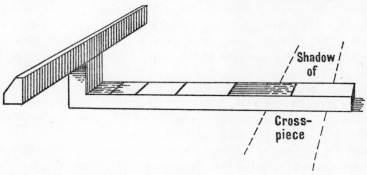

This sun clock divided the day into twelve hours, six in the forenoon and six in the afternoon. The cross-piece at the top was turned to the east in the morning and to the west in the afternoon, so that the shadow shortened as morning advanced and grew longer from noon until night.

Most ancient peoples divided the natural day and night into twelve hours each, so that the length of the hour varied according to the season. In the summer the day hours were longer and the hours of night were shorter, and in the winter the opposite applied. Why the number twelve was chosen is not really known, but probably it was that it was so easily divisible by 3, 4, and 6.

There were many different types of sundial used. A Babylonian priest is said to have constructed a hollow hemisphere something like a bowl, and to have arranged a tiny sphere above it to cast a shadow. By dividing the path described by the sphere's shadow into twelve equal parts and by drawing some rather complicated curves, he was able to divide the day into that number of hours.

As the gnomon did not cast a clear shadow, the Egyptians often used their obelisks for calculations concerning the heavens as well as for calculations involving time, while the Greeks, like the Babylonian priest, often used a gnomon with a small sphere at the top, the centre of its shadow being taken as the centre of the Sun.

THE WATER CLOCK OR CLEPSYDRA

The sundial was not a very consistent instrument for measuring time, for it was no use at night or on cloudy days, and of course the sunrises and sunsets vary from day to day. There was a great need for some means of telling the passage of the hours in cloudy weather and at night, so a device based on the flow of water was introduced.

We do not know when this was introduced, but at first it was probably an earthenware vessel made with a tiny hole through which the water flowed into another vessel used for measuring. But this also had its disadvantages, for the more water in the first container, the more quickly it would flow out, and therefore it was not very accurate. So later a glass vessel was used, and it was arranged to keep the container full by means of a further container.

Water clocks are known to have been in use in Egypt in 1400 B.C., and later there were several variations of them. One clepsydra, the proper name for a water clock, made at Alexandria, was arranged on a system of cogs which caused a pointer to show the hour of the day. This was about 140 B.C., but hundreds of years later in A.D. 807 the Arabian caliph Haroun-al-Raschid is said to have sent an ingenious water clock to the French king Charlemagne.

OTHER FORMS

If we do not actually possess one, we have all seen pictures of an hour glass. This was a very useful invention that was extremely popular until clocks and watches became available just over two hundred years ago. It was merely a glass tube so pinched at the waist that fine grains of sand could trickle through the tiny hole at a constant rate, and when the upper container was emptied the instrument was reversed. There is still in existence a picture of one in Rome which is dated about 300 B.C., while in the Middle Ages they were always to be seen in monasteries. Variations of them are still in use today, as you know, and one is even used in the House of Commons to warn the members that a vote will be taken when the sand runs out at two minutes.

The lamp clock, the hour candle, and even a metal ring with a small hole through which a beam of sunlight showed up a small number, were other means that have been in use at various times.

The lamp clock was so arranged that the flame used up a certain amount of oil in a certain time, this being clearly indicated, while the hour candle, said to have been invented by King Alfred, was based on the same principle, being marked to show intervals of one hour.

CLOCKS

We should not think that clocks based on wheels were unknown till after Galileo, for the Romans are said to have had
them and they are known to have been in use in some churches
by the 7th century. In the 13th century clocks were beginning
to look like those of today, and in 1379 the father of modern
clocks was built by a German, Heinrich de Vick, at the royal
palace of King Charles V of France. Its motivating principle
was a 500-lb. weight suspended by a cord which was wound
round a cylinder. This weight communicated power to geared
wheels, and there was a checking device to make sure that the
weight did not descend too quickly.

But this was not the first based on this principle, for an arch-
deacon of Verona, in Italy, is said to have invented a clock based
on this principle as early as the 9th century. Even portable clocks
were known in England by the 15th century.

In 1581 Galileo discovered the isochronism of the pendulum,
though an Arab, Ibn Yunis, had noted this 400 years earlier.
The pendulum clock was chiefly due to the Dutch mathematician Christiaan Huygens about 1657, and so the basic system of
our modern clocks, excluding electric ones, was established.

7: A SHORT HISTORY OF ORDINARY ENGLISH WEIGHTS AND MEASURES

LENGTH AND AREA

In the time of the Anglo-Saxons measurements of length varied from place to place. For smaller measurements there were the thumb, roughly one inch, the span, about nine inches, the cubit, the distance from the elbow to the tip of the middle finger on the average man, the foot and the pace.

The foot in use might be the Roman foot of 11·65 inches or the Northern foot of 13·2 inches, and there were also a Greek foot and a Pythic foot. The foot most commonly in use by the Saxons, however, was the Northern foot.

A unit of the Romans was known as the 'as', and when this was divided into twelve fractional parts each part was called an uncia. Therefore when the Saxons divided their foot into twelve equal parts they called each part an 'ynce'—later an inch—but they also divided the foot into four palms and thirty-six barleycorns.

For land measurement the Saxons used the rod. This was equivalent to fifteen Northern feet, and forty of these land rods made up a furrow-length or furlong, from the Saxon 'furlang'. Though the Northern foot is no longer in use, the land rod and the furlong remain the same in length.

The term yard is from an old English word 'yerd', meaning a stick or rod. According to an old account King Henry I measured the length of his arm and said that this should be the standard length of the yard, and some belief is attached to this by some authorities.

The word mile has come down to us from the Romans, to whom it meant 1,000 paces or the equivalent of 1,620 yards.

In 1305 Edward I set down our present system of linear measure and had a standard measure made to which all others could be brought for comparison. His statute, or order, is quite interesting. It said:

'Three grains of barley dry and round make one inch, twelve inches one foot, three feet an ulna, five and a half ulnae make a rod, and forty rods in length and four in breadth make an acre.'

The ulna, which is the Latin name for one of the bones in the forearm and originally meant the elbow—and so 'ell'—was later known as the yard, and it is rather surprising to know that the standard measure of Edward I would not differ from our present standard by more than 0·04 of an inch.

This new foot was an attempt to keep everyone satisfied. In the measure of land by area the standard unit was the acre, which was usually understood as a 'morning's plowing', a strip of land four rods wide and a furrow long, or four rods by forty, that is 160 square rods. Therefore the measure of five and a half ulnae was necessary to keep the acre exactly as before, for any alteration of the length of the rod itself or the area of the acre would have met with strong opposition.

The introduction of the perch, '5 Yardes and a half', and the 'Rodde of land, 1 Perche in bredth and 40 in length' according to Robert Recorde, seems to have taken place in the late 13th century.

In 1497 Henry VII confirmed Edward I's ulna, and he provided a standard yard. It is now in the Science Museum in London, and is an 'end' measure, being only 0·037 of an inch shorter overall than our present one. In 1588 Queen Elizabeth I provided another new standard, defining the yard as thirty-six inches and the cloth ell as 45 inches. Elizabeth's standard is only 0·01 of an inch short of our present Imperial Standard, which was made legal in 1855 and defined as being correct at 62° Fahrenheit with the barometer standing at 30 inches of mercury. It is remarkable that since 1305 the yard has only varied 0·04 of an inch, or 1 mm.

CAPACITY MEASURE

We have no definite knowledge of the capacity measures of the Saxons, but there must have been some in existence, for William I and subsequent kings stated that both weights and measures then in being would not be changed.

With all these weights and measures you will notice that five dates are usually mentioned. They are the dates of various statutes or laws set down by the monarch of the time, except for the last, and are as follows:

1266—Henry III; 1305—Edward I; 1497—Henry VII; 1601—Queen Elizabeth I; 1824—Imperial Standard.

In 1497 Henry VII set the whole system of measures on a firm basis by supplying copies of his standard to forty-three cities for reference. He also set up the Winchester Standard, and by means of this each measure was defined by weight in Troy ounces of its content of wheat. The pint had to consist of $12\frac{1}{2}$ Troy ounces, the quart 25 Troy ounces, the 'pottle' 4 pints, the gallon 8 pints, and the bushel 64 pints, that is, 800 Troy ounces of wheat.

His measure for the bushel and gallon are still in the Science Museum in London, and are the oldest English capacity measures in existence.

Queen Elizabeth confirmed these measures in her statute and issued copies to sixty cities. The measures remained in force till 1824 when a new gallon was set up. This was defined as 'The volume of 10 avoirdupois pounds of distilled water weighed in air at 62° Fahrenheit with the barometer standing at 30 inches of mercury.' In addition, the gallon was defined as the basic unit for all other measures of capacity, both dry measure and liquid, and from that time the measure became known as the Imperial standard. Its difference from that of Henry VII is an increase in volume of three per cent.

WEIGHTS

The weight system of the Saxons was rather similar to that of the Arabs, except that 20 so-called pennyweights were equal to 450 grains instead of 10 dirhems, from which we get our name drachm. The pound weight was made up of 12 ounces each of 450 grains, and as such was known as the 'moneyer's pound', though there was also a 'silver' pound which consisted of 240 silver pence of 225 grains. As you would expect, the pennyweight was the weight of a silver penny, for coins often did duty as weights as well as being a means of exchange.

The name of pound is derived from a Latin word 'pondo' (by weight), while the ounce is derived from the Latin 'uncia', being one-twelfth of a Roman pound. William I confirmed these weights of the Saxons after the Norman conquest.

The statute of Henry III stated in effect:

The English penny which is called a sterlyng, round and uncut, ought to weigh 32 grains of wheate taken from the middle of the ear. And the ounce to weigh 20 pennies. And 12 ounces make the London pound, that is to say 20 shillings sterlyng.

The avoirdupois system was introduced from Bayonne in France about 1300, though it was probably of Spanish origin. It was originally applied to the weighing of bulky goods, but was gradually used as a separate system of weight from coin or bullion, and became more commonly used.

Edward III established a new system of weights, including a pound of 6,993 grains and an ounce of 437 grains for wool weighing. The Troy pound was first mentioned in official records in 1414 by Henry V, who simplified the exchange between the two systems, making 15 Troy ounces of 480 grains equal 16 avoirdupois ounces of 450 grains.

Henry VII again confirmed these standards, sending out copies to the cities as before, and stating that wool weighing was now to be done on avoirdupois weight, but the ounce was to be one of 7,000 grains.

However, in 1574 the citizens of London complained that 'the weights used throughout this our realm are uncertain and varying one from another, to the great slander of our realm'. So Elizabeth appointed a jury of twenty-one men to construct new standards, and, when these failed, a second jury in 1582.

The outcome was a new set of standards, both in Troy and avoirdupois, and 57 copies of these were completed by 1588. The hundredweight was settled as 112 pounds, and the ton as 20 hundredweights. The exchequer sets consisted of flat and bell-shaped weights and they were still in use in 1824, being based on the pound of 16 ounces, each of 7,000 grains. They were subsequently found to be deficient by only a small fraction of 1 per cent.

By the Weights and Measures Act of 1878 the Troy pound was abolished, but not the Troy ounce of 480 grains, which is still used for precious metals and stones.

8: THE INTRODUCTION OF THE METRIC SYSTEM

THERE were many different systems of measuring before the introduction of the metric system, not only in different countries, but often in each country itself, for in France alone there were at one time eighteen different ways of measuring cloth. Before there was much improvement in means of transport this may not have proved too irksome, but as communications between countries improved and were speeded up, it was realized that these differences hampered the development of trade.

Several people saw the need to unify the system of measuring in different countries, and attempts were made in this direction from the 13th century onwards. One of the best ideas was that of a clergyman of Lyons in France, Gabriel Mouton. In 1670 he proposed a decimal system having as its basis the length of an arc one minute of the earth's circumference. He suggested that this unit should be called a milliare or mille, and that larger and smaller measurements could be determined by multiplying this by tens or by subdivision by tens. This idea is very similar to the modern system.

Other suggestions about the same time were that of taking the length of a pendulum which was beating seconds, or a pendulum which was beating half-seconds, and these ideas were taken up so seriously during the next one hundred years that in 1789 the French Academy of Science investigated the whole matter with the later encouragement of the French parliament.

The idea of using the length of a pendulum was discarded in favour of taking a line on the earth's surface. A survey was made of the length of a line from the North Pole to the equator running through Dunkirk in France and Barcelona in Spain. Though the calculation was not quite correct, this distance was divided into ten million parts, and one of these was called a metre or 'measure'. This, as you know, is equivalent to 39·37 inches, and it became known as the standard metre.

For smaller measurements they divided the metre by multiples of ten, and for larger measurements multiplied it in the same way. When dividing they decided to give a Latin prefix to the new part, as deci-, centi-, milli-, and when they multiplied the metre they used Greek prefixes, Deka-, Hecto-, Kilo-.

It was a very simple matter to use the metre and its parts for area and volumes, so that we speak of square kilometres, cubic centimetres, and so on, but for liquid measure a cubic vessel of exactly ten centimetres on each side was used, so that its volume was a thousand cubic centimetres. The amount of water that this vessel would hold was then called a litre, and this, again, could be subdivided and multiplied into decilitres, decalitres, and so on.

For a standard unit of weight one cubic centimetre of pure water at its maximum density—just before it freezes, or at 4° Centigrade—was used. This was called the gramme, and a platinum cylinder known as the 'kilogramme of the archives' was declared as the standard for one thousand grammes, the same prefixes being used for multiplication and division as with length and capacity.

In 1840 this system, the only scientific method of weighing and measuring in the world, was made compulsory in France. In 1875, however, a new agreement called the Metric Treaty set up a new standard for the metre and the kilogramme. The new metre consisted of a bar of ninety per cent. platinum and ten per cent. iridium, and was made up of these metals because of the resultant rigidity, being called the 'international prototype metre'.

When the first kilogramme was made it was impossible to measure the volume of water of a cubic decimetre to a one-millionth part, and because of this there is not now the exact comparison between the metre, the kilogramme and the litre that was intended in the first place. If a certain volume of water is measured by linear dimensions, and is also weighed, the two results do not coincide exactly, but differ by 28 parts in 1,000,000.

The litre is therefore now defined as the volume of a kilogramme of pure water at its maximum density and under standard pressure, and it is equivalent to 1·000028 cubic decimetres, though for most practical purposes this slight difference can be ignored.

The last stage in the history of the metric system was reached in 1927, when an international conference on weights and measures adopted an additional definition of the metre in terms of the wave length of light.

The metric system is now used by almost every civilized country except England and America, but even in these two countries scientists use the method freely. If it were generally adopted it would soon prove more convenient, less costly and quicker than our present system.

9: THE GROWTH OF MATHEMATICS THROUGH SOCIAL NEEDS

IF you have read through the first three books carefully you must have noticed how the development of mathematics was often connected with the various needs of a particular time, most especially up to the 16th century. To put this into other words, we may say that the growth of mathematics was related to social needs.

You have read that in early Mesopotamia the temple was an important centre, not only of religion, but of learning and business. But some knowledge of mathematics is essential before you can even have a temple. Some kind of plans, however crude, have to be drawn up, measurements laid out, materials have to be brought to the site, and hundreds of workers engaged.

Plans of the temple were made to scale, often by means of a coloured string. Such a plan has actually been discovered in the ancient city of Erech in Sumeria, and others have been found on loose clay tablets, the Sumerians believing that they had been drawn up by their gods; while the foundations were also marked out with string before the building was begun. Quite obviously, these operations involved some accepted standard of measurement, and some system of calculation.

In the finished temple accounts had to be kept by the priests, not only concerning that of the temple itself, but showing also the amount of business transacted, for, as we have just said, the temple was a centre of commerce as well as of religion, and was also the place to which all government taxes had to be paid. Such a widespread organization as this, the calculation of taxes payable, the paying-in of goods and later money, the issuing of receipts, and the working out of the seasons and feast days, required a considerable knowledge of some form of arithmetic.

When we read that one tribal god, this really meant the temple, owned what amounted to seventeen square miles of land, three-quarters of which was allocated in plots to families, and that the 'god' also possessed twenty-one bakers with their female slaves, twenty-five brewers with their assistants, in addition to spinners, weavers, clerks and priests, we realize that this arithmetic must have been fairly considerable.

Furthermore, in working out their various problems they soon discovered that certain quantities and numbers came up again and again, so they kept a record of these common problems and their answers for further reference to save time in the future, and thus the first mathematical tables were built up.

In Egypt a somewhat similar system existed, but with the leader of the tribe or nation, not a servant of the god, but looked upon as the god himself. So in this case, the pharaoh received the taxes of the people, and these were much greater than those of the Mesopotamians. With such a large surplus the pharaoh was able to do things on a bigger scale. He had fine buildings and even canals constructed, and navies of large ships built, and even kept a civil service for the recording of receipts and expenses.

The carrying out of such projects was bound to encourage interest in, and the development of, arithmetic and geometry. To cut a canal or work out a large drainage system a good knowledge of mensuration, levelling and surveying is necessary, and by the efficient way in which they accomplished these things, the Egyptians showed that they fully understood the fundamentals of such subjects. As we read on p. 26, much of this ability was acquired through the social need of having to re-divide the land after each flooding of the river Nile.

They soon learnt also how to estimate approximately the amount of seed required to sow a field of a given size, and how much grain was required to fill a granary, or containers of certain shapes. They were able to calculate various areas and volumes from these experiences, and in addition could estimate how many bricks were necessary for a wall of specified dimensions or for other buildings.

N

They took a great interest in the stars, not for its own sake but because they felt that the destiny of their king and their country was bound up with their movements in the heavens, and as a result of their studies learnt many useful things regarding geometry, and angles of elevation in particular.

Before the pharaoh died, sometimes at the beginning of his reign, he decided to build a great tomb for himself that would also be a lasting memorial. This had to be built to exact measurements and to a definite plan. The four sides must face the four cardinal points of the compass, the four corners at the base must be exact right angles (the Great Pyramid, the one we are referring to, is only $\frac{3}{500}$ of a degree out). The perimeter of the base must be in a definite ratio to the height, that of 2π, while a ventilating shaft must be at right angles to the south face and allow the light of the Dog Star, Sirius (the one that heralded the flooding of the Nile), to shine on the head of the dead king. All this was achieved, showing an amazing knowledge of practical geometry and an astounding degree of accuracy.

When we come to the Greeks and their advanced civilization, we must remember that they learnt a great deal from the Egyptians and Mesopotamians, but their number system, you may remember, was rather cumbersome, so they directed their efforts more to the study of geometry. In this they were encouraged more by social conditions than by social need, but the wealthy slave owners and merchants found ample time to experiment with geometrical figures, and to work out reasons 'why' for many facts which earlier peoples had known but could not be bothered, or were unable, to prove.

In their study of astronomy, so necessary for the farmer in the regulation of the calendar, they found that the stars appeared to trace out figures which could be drawn, and by means of these figures and the geometrical rules they had worked out, they found that they could locate planets in the heavens and steer their ships more accurately.

Under Alexander the Great the Greeks prospered as never before. Large ships were constructed, good ports and towns were built, and trade and industry and power developed to such an extent that it became possible to set up seats of learning and to pay people to study and work in them.

So we come to Alexandria, with its professional scientists and teachers, with its Euclid, Eratosthenes, Archimedes and others. You may remember the work of Archimedes in his Measure of the Circle. It is more than likely that he found himself obliged to come to some closer understanding of π than that known up to his time for his work in mechanics, and it is just as probable that some of his other discoveries were made in working out problems with which he had been confronted, such as the launching of the large ship built by King Hiero II, or the 'engines of war' which were necessary to keep the Romans at bay.

As longer voyages made known more of the world, some felt that a more exact estimation of the size of the earth was necessary, so Eratosthenes and others worked out original calculations in this direction, and drew up maps which were considerable improvements on those used before.

When we consider the mathematics of India we find social needs again having an influence. The Hindus traded widely, and their mathematicians were very interested in problems involving trade, such as interest and taxation, variation of prices, debt and losses. From the works of Bhaskara, for instance, we can learn that interest to be paid on money varied from $3\frac{1}{2}$ to 5 per cent., while prices of food and labour are also discussed. We are even told the prices of slaves, and we can learn that a female slave was worth most when sixteen years old, and her value then fell away as she grew older; moreover, to calculate her value at any time after sixteen involved a problem on inverse proportion. It would seem that the average value of such a slave at her best age was equivalent to eight oxen that had been working for two years.

Having to deal with large numbers sometimes in rather involved calculations, the Hindus felt the need for a number system that was adequate enough to make such problems solvable without the necessity of a bead frame.

Strangely enough, the fact that they had inherited no cultural background, in other words had to start from the beginning of things, served them in good stead. For they gradually evolved an entirely new system, quite unlike any other before it, based on tens and position, and with their vital 'sunya' or zero. They needed to set down large numbers almost as soon as they had learnt to write at all. So their unique system came about. It was soon followed by a desire to form rules for even quicker and easier methods, and as a result the science of algebra took root, though earlier peoples had held similar ideas but used different methods.

Later, in the Middle Ages, we find that the trade of Europe had centred around the Mediterranean, and particularly in Italy. We would expect, therefore, some contribution to the further development of mathematics to come from this quarter; and so it does.

It was Fibonacci, the son of an Italian merchant, who introduced the new Hindu-Arabic numerals into Italy and so into Christian Europe, and the advantages of this system over the existing one meant that the Italian merchants began to use them in their calculations, though not without great opposition.

This use of the new symbols by Italian merchants marks the beginning of modern business arithmetic, for this method gradually encouraged them to develop a more methodical system of book-keeping, and of arranging the various problems of arithmetic which they met in the course of their transactions into various categories, such as ratio, or proportion, interest, profit and loss and so on. In addition, they simplified some of the methods used in arithmetic, and limited its basic operations to seven, which they called numeration, addition, subtraction, multiplication, division, raising to powers, and extraction of roots.

Even in the 16th and 17th centuries the influence of social requirements was still present. The use of better cannon in warfare necessitated the use of geometry and trigonometry in order to be able to use the weapon with a greater measure of accuracy.

The needs of navigators, travelling farther and farther across hitherto unknown seas to expand trade, meant that more intricate instruments must be made and a deeper interest in astronomy developed. As these inventions came into being, including the compass, clocks and the many other instruments used in the expanding sciences which required greater degrees of accuracy than ever before, so we find that mathematics is being stretched to finer limits, moving into higher fields as a consequence, and becoming an inseparable servant of the scientist.

10: THE INFLUENCE OF ASTRONOMY ON THE GROWTH OF MATHEMATICS

MAN'S first study of astronomy was made through necessity rather than out of interest. Early man needed to know when to sow his grain and to do other things connected with farming, and therefore when to expect the seasons. As we have read, one of the first results of this study of the heavens was to establish a calendar based on the behaviour of the moon, for it was seen that a certain number of moons would appear between one dry season and the next.

Later it was seen that it was possible to work out the length of the year also by means of the sun's shadow, for by noting the day of its shortest shadow—namely the summer solstice—and waiting for this shortest shadow to appear again, it was found that a definite number of days elapsed.

With early peoples this counting and recording of the seasons was usually left to the priests, and while it was fairly easy to count cattle and sheep on the fingers or by means of stones, it was a much more difficult matter to record the passage of days and months and years without some kind of a number system. One of the first influences of astronomy, therefore, was to encourage the development of a system of numbers.

As this business of time-recording developed, men next felt the need for a more accurate system of measuring. The Egyptians later discovered that the star Sirius heralded the flooding of the river Nile, and naturally began to calculate their year from the first rising of this star. Soon they worked out means of calculating just where this star would rise on the horizon, and after this when to expect the rising of other stars and groups of stars, or constellations as they are called.

Such work first required a fixing of the four cardinal points of the compass. This was done, as you read in Book One, by measuring the length of the sun's shadow, and once these points were established the idea of angles arose, and was later extended to a more accurate system of measurement by dividing angles up into much smaller units.

Our division of the circle into 360 degrees most probably arose from the fact that the ancients believed that the sun travelled round the earth once in every 360 days, and divided its apparent path into 360 parts, one for each day.

The more man studied the stars the more he became interested in them, for he began to feel that just as they controlled the seasons, so they also controlled his destiny. The movements of the stars, and especially the planets, were now most carefully studied, and from these movements numerous calculations were made involving a good knowledge of arithmetic and geometry, particularly the measurement of angles.

We notice this in detail with the Greeks, who did not hesitate to bring their knowledge of geometry to bear on the study of the heavens. So we have Aristarchus working out the angular distance between the sun and the moon, when the latter is exactly at half moon, and being only 2° 21′ out, and also working out a ratio of distances of the sun and the moon from the earth.

There is also Eratosthenes, who used angle measurement to determine the size of the earth, and thus showed men how much more of the world there was left to discover. His map of the world, with its lines of latitude and longitude, ranks him as the founder of scientific geography.

He was followed by the great astronomer Hipparchus, who determined the year within six minutes of its true length, calculated the inclination of the ecliptic (the sun's apparent path, you may remember) to within five minutes of a degree, and worked out several other astronomical data to a near accuracy. Hipparchus also set down a table of chords of arcs, similar to our sines, for his work on astronomy, and he showed such ability in working with these that he is called the inventor of trigonometry.

Ptolemy of Alexandria, who lived about A.D. 100, was another famous astronomer who contributed to mathematics. Most of his work was founded on that of Hipparchus, but he set it down in a more systematic way. His work, called the *Almagest*, was composed of thirteen books, the first of which dealt with trigonometry, both plane and spherical (triangles on a spherical surface), and a table of chords, while he uses degrees, minutes and seconds in the measurement of angles. The other books were on the shape of the earth, the movements of heavenly bodies, eclipses and other phenomena. It became a standard work on astronomy until the 16th century, and in it Ptolemy showed the application of geometry to astronomy, and his own ability as a geometrician.

The Hindu mathematicians were also interested in astronomy. Three of the four books of Arya-Bhata, for instance, are on this subject and elementary spherical trigonometry, while Brahmagupta's work, the *Siddhanta*, was mostly on astronomy, though two chapters were devoted to arithmetic, algebra and geometry.

Navigation also brought its influence to bear on both astronomy and mathematics. In the early days sailors merely followed the coastline till they arrived at their destination, but later when they were able to calculate the latitude of the place they wanted, they sailed for this line of latitude and kept on it as nearly as they could, sailing east or west until they reached the end of their journey. They were able to find their latitude by calculating the altitude of the Pole Star, but finding a position of longitude was impossible until accurate time-keeping could be adopted.

Astronomy was thus of extreme importance in good navigation, and so an even deeper interest was taken in the heavens. Star maps had been made by even the early astronomers, but they were now seen to have a practical use. In the 15th century, the Crown Prince of Portugal, known later as Henry the Navigator, built an observatory at Cape St Vincent and began there a school of seamanship. For the preparation of star and other maps, and the making of nautical tables and instruments, he engaged Arab map makers and Jewish astronomers, some of whom had stayed behind when the Arabs—or more correctly, the Moors—had been driven out of Spain, and these men also instructed the navigators of the ships that Henry sent out on explorations in the new methods that were being worked out in the school.

In such work it became very necessary to know just where the planets and certain stars could be located, and when such people as Copernicus, Tycho Brahe and Kepler later worked out astronomical tables of great accuracy showing that the position of the planets can be determined, astronomy made another important stride forward.

We have dealt previously with the work of Kepler in this connection, and of how he applied geometric constructions to the movements of the planets, and even used an advanced method of finding the areas of the focal sectors of ellipses, a clever extension of the old Greek geometry.

So as the science of astronomy expands we find that, even in the works of Sir Isaac Newton, mathematics—and geometry in particular—is applied more and more to fit the new findings, and later, when the differential calculus is developed and better understood, higher mathematics goes hand in hand with advanced astronomy.

TYPICAL EXAMINATION QUESTIONS
BASED ON BOOK IV

1. Write an essay on either of the following:
   (a) The history of English Weights and Measures.
   (b) The history of π.

2. Give an account, illustrated by a sketch, of any mechanical aid to calculation used in early times.

3. Describe the influence of (i) astronomy, (ii) navigation on the growth of mathematics.

4. Write a short account of the introduction of the metric system.

5. Give an account of the methods of recording time before the invention of clocks.

6. Describe the influence of astronomy on the growth of mathematics.

7. Write a short account of the influence on mathematics of trade and commerce between Italy and the East in the Middle Ages.

8. Write an essay on:
 (a) The origin and development of the more common of our present-day weights and measures,
or
 (b) The development of mathematics as a direct result of particular problems or social needs.

9. Trace the development of the symbols for the common operations in arithmetic and algebra.

10. Give an account of ONE of the following:
 (a) Ancient methods of recording time.
 (b) Early calculating machines.
 (c) Early attempts to find the value of π.

11. Describe some of the impulses towards mathematics among the earliest civilizations such as the Sumerian or Egyptian. In what way did the social needs of the times influence its growth?

12. Write short notes on the abacus.

13. Give an account of the influences leading to the development of trigonometry.

14. Discuss the ways in which the arithmetic of various countries met the commercial needs of the times.

15. Give an account of the early history of the slide rule and explain briefly the principles underlying its use for multiplication and division.

16. Write an essay on the history and development of the metric system.

17. Where was mathematics studied before 1000 B.C.? Give a brief account of the work done and suggest reasons for it.

18. Describe and explain the use of Napier's Rods or Bones.

19. Write short notes on *three* ways in which mathematics has been influenced by the needs of mankind.

INDEX

ABACUS, 40, 79, 83, 157
Abscissa, 136
Abu Kamil, 144
Acceleration, 136
Adams, 138
Addition, sign for, 29, 58, 144, 145
Adelard of Bath, 85
Ahmes Papyrus, 21, 27, 143, 149, 153
Al Battam, 151
Alchemists, 83
Alexander the Great, 31, 46, 184
Alexandria, 46, 185, 189
   Destruction of, 74
Algebra, 15, 48, 58, 66, 77, 81, 89, 143
Algebraic curves, 131
Algorismus, *see* Alkarismi
Aliquot parts, 13, 22
Al jabr, 77
Alkarismi, 76, 85, 144
Al Kashi, 155
Al-Khowarazmi, *see* Alkarismi
Almagest, 57, 151, 190
Al Mamun, 75
Analytical geometry, 115, 120, 129
Anglo-Saxon measurements, 174
Apollonius, 54, 75
Arabs, 13, 55, 74, 85, 144, 147
Archimedes, 51, 75, 106, 115, 153, 154, 185
Areas, measurement of, 13, 174
Aristarchus, 149
Aristotle, 20
Arithmetic, 14, 80, 83, 98
   Progressions, *see* Progressions
Arithmetica, 58
   Infinitorum, 128
   Integra, 91
Armillary spheres, 49
Ars Magna, 144
Arya-Bhata, 66, 143, 151, 154, 190
As, 174
Asia Minor, 10, 31
Assyria, 7, 10
Astrology, 16
Astronomy, influence on mathematics, 16, 33, 63, 66, 108, 110, 151, 166, 184, 188
Augustus Caesar, 169

Avoirdupois measures, 177
Axioms, 37

BABYLON, 7, 8, 143, 149, 153
Bagdad, 74, 144
Banks, 10
Bead frame, 40; *see* Abacus
Bernoulli, Jacques, 136, 137
Bhaskara, 68, 87, 143, 147
Binomial expression, 126
   Theorem, 129, 131
Bissaker, Robert, 164
Bombelli, 144, 147
Bones or rods, Napier's, 161
Brackets, 148
Brahe, Tycho, 110, 191
Brahmagupta, 67, 143, 154, 155
Briggs, Henry, 95
Brokerage, 87
Burgi, Jobst, 98
Bushel, 176

CAESAR, JULIUS, 63, 168
Calculating machines, 124, 156
Calculation, methods of, 13
Calculus, infinitesimal, 113, 120, 127, 128, 130, 132, 135, 136
   of probabilities, 137
Calendar, 63, 166, 184
Capacity measures, 176
Cardan, 144
Cavalieri, 128
Centres of gravity, 129
Chaldeans, 7, 17, 166
China, 3, 35, 155, 157, 162
Chords of circles, 150
Chung-chih, 155
Circle, measurement of, 13, 43, 52, 55, 153, 185, 189; *see also* Quadrature of Curvi-linear figures *and* Pi
   Quadrature of, 42, 129
Cissoid, 118, 120, 129
Classical Problems, Three, 41
Clepsydra, 171
Clocks, 173
Colour, 131
Colours (unknown quantities), 69
Combinations, 120